Kate Percy's
Go
Faster
Food
for your
Active Family

Go Faster Food for your Active Family
Previously released as Go Faster Food for Kids

First Edition
Published in the UK in September 2013
by Go Faster Food Ltd
13-14 Orchard Street
Bristol
BS1 5EH

www.katepercys.com

A CIP catalogue record of this book is available from the British Library.

FSC
www.fsc.org
MIX
Paper from
responsible sources
FSC® C014540

Book designed and set by Rose-Innes Designs.
Printed and bound in the UK by Cambrian Printers Ltd.
Photography by Ewelina Karbowiak of Karezona Photography,
unless otherwise indicated.

ISBN 978-0-9574168-2-6

For further information on books published by Go Faster Food Ltd
visit www.katepercys.com

Dedication

I would like to dedicate this book to my three children, Helena, James and William. They each take their busy and demanding schedule of training for their various sports – athletics, football, kayaking, rowing, rugby, swimming and tennis – in their stride and with great enthusiasm, successfully squeezing it around their academic and social lives. Helping them combine all this activity with healthy and appropriate eating is a challenge that I relish and that has ultimately been the inspiration behind this book.

Acknowledgements

My thanks go to:

The seriously impressive Go Faster Kids who have shared their training and eating habits with me.

Ewelina Karbowiak (Evie) of Karezona Photography for her imaginative photography, and for making our photo shoots such fun.

Sue Baic, Msc RD RNutr, dietitian and brilliant, supportive nutritional advisor.

David Stone, of TSPM Ltd, for his expertise and invaluable support.

Michelle, Kate and Melanie, the team at Rose-Innes Designs, for their fabulous ideas and attention to detail.

Mark Scoble of Constellation Media for his advice and encouragement.

My mum and dad, a.k.a. Brenda and John Percy, for kindling my interest in food and cooking in the first place.

My wonderful husband, Mark, for motivating me to run my first marathon, and whose steadfast support for Go Faster Food has never faltered.

Contents

Welcome from Kate Percy

What, when and how much a child eats is not only the starting block to better performance in sport, it is also the key to good concentration, attainment at school and improved sleep quality. It boosts recovery after training and reduces susceptibility to injury too. Making the right food choices enables children to be the best they can be, in sport and in life.

Combining my experiences as a cook, an athlete and a mother with the latest scientific evidence, I have written *Go Faster Food for your Active Family* as a guide for parents, teachers, coaches and, of course, active children themselves, on how to eat for good health and optimum sports performance.

My interest in food for sport was kindled when my husband, Mark, was training for the New York Marathon in 2000. His preparation started well, but he became tired, even lethargic, as his training progressed. I decided to study sports nutrition. With more sustaining food and by tweaking the timing of meals around his runs to promote recovery, Mark began to feel more energised. His running improved massively and, as the family grew, it was clear that we were all benefitting from this better understanding of what and when to eat. Having played the dutiful wife to the heroic marathon runner far too long, I resolved to try out this running game for myself. I very quickly caught the bug and six months later was being cheered through Harlem in the New York Marathon! To date this has led to a further six marathons and 'good for age' entry into prestigious marathons such as Boston and London, as well as the publication of my first book, *Go Faster Food*.

Direct experience with my three children has been the motivation behind *Go Faster Food for your Active Family*. My daughter, Helena, rows for her college and sprints and hurdles for Cambridge University. My elder son, James, plays school 1st XV and club rugby, whilst my younger son, Will, is at his happiest in a kayak, surfing the waves, river-running on white water and playing kayak polo.

Having sporty children with regular training commitments can make family life a frenetic whirlwind of activity. It is hard enough finding time to prepare healthy weekday meals, let alone to sit down to eat them! It is this challenge that inspired me to develop a selection of healthy recipes designed specifically to help children achieve their personal best; tasty, nutritionally balanced and, most importantly, practical recipes appropriate for children and the whole family alike.

I'd like my nutrition tips to motivate children to think seriously about what foods to eat for their sport so they can train, perform and recover stronger, and I hope my recipes will power them through their training and competitions with a smile on their face.

Enjoy cooking up some great sporting success!

© Kornilovdream | Dreamstime.com

Introduction

All children need calories to fuel the healthy development of their bodies and brains. Active children, however, need to eat more calories. They need calories to support basic growth and development, then additional calories to fuel their sport. In fact, children training for as little as an hour a day will need around 500 additional calories. These need to be nutrient-rich, packed with goodness to sustain energy levels, and well balanced with the appropriate amount of carbohydrate, protein and fat.

The optimal timing of eating and drinking is also key. Children need fuel:

- before sport to provide the correct level of energy
- during sport to sustain this energy
- after sport to promote quick recovery

This combination of eating the right foods at the right time will enable children to perform to the best of their abilities.

The food we serve our children will influence their eating habits and consequently their health, not just now, but also for the rest of their lives. Childhood, according to the British Heart Foundation, is when the pernicious seed of heart disease and obesity is sown. Encourage a child to be active and to enjoy and understand the benefits of a balanced and varied diet and you'll teach them good habits for life. The earlier this is achieved, the earlier children can make their own informed decisions.

Children rely on the adults around them for their food. Whether we have children of our own, coach, teach or care for children, it is our responsibility as adults to pass on an understanding of good eating habits. We decide what our children eat at home and what food goes into the fridge and the kitchen cupboards. There are no excuses. Ultimately, the buck stops with us!

Of course, this is easier said than done. No two children are the same. Some are willing to try a wide variety of foods and appear constantly hungry; others can be picky, leaving parents desperate for ideas. Good or bad eater, when it comes to providing a child with healthy, nutritionally balanced meals and snacks within the frenzied framework of before-, during- and after-school activities, family commitments and work life, there are times when most of us struggle with how, what and when to feed our children.

Supported by an abundance of practical 'Go Faster' eating tips, Part One of *Go Faster Food for your Active Family* advises on what constitutes a healthy diet for active children. It also considers the more specific nutritional requirements for training and competition.

In Part Two, this nutritional theory is brought to life. With a host of tasty, imaginative and easy-to-prepare recipes, you will find the essential toolkit to fuel kids through their busy lives.

Nutritious and delicious food to help children achieve their full potential!

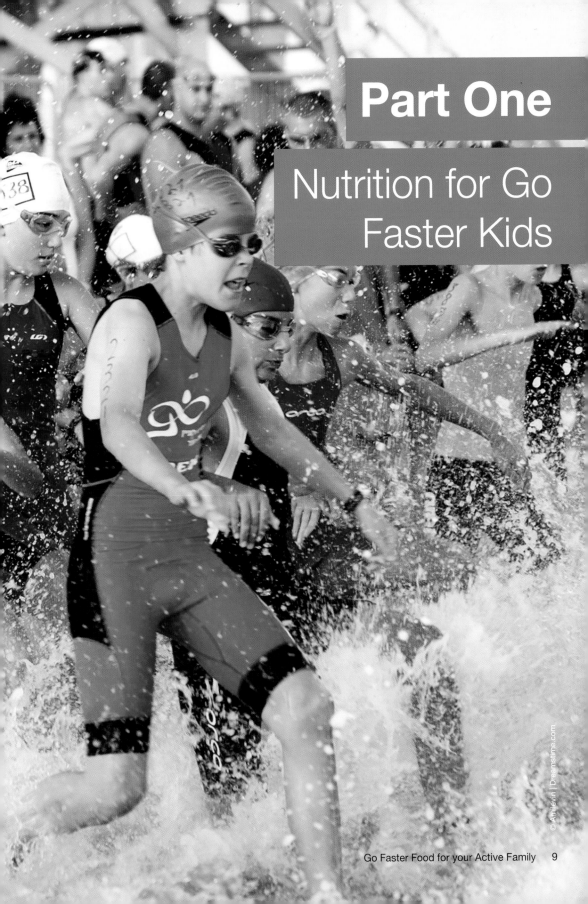

Part One

Nutrition for Go Faster Kids

Top Ten Eating Tips for Go Faster Kids

1. Balance and Variety

Food provides a range of nutrients, all of which the body needs in differing amounts. Some nutrients supply energy whilst others are essential for the growth and the maintenance of the body.

Our basic nutritional requirements are provided by the three macronutrients - carbohydrate, protein and fat. Not only do these equip the body with energy, they are also important for the growth and maintenance of a child's body.

Micronutrients, or vitamins and minerals, are essential for keeping us healthy, but are needed in smaller amounts. Vitamins, such as the B vitamins, help the body utilise other nutrients in the correct way, and minerals help build and maintain the body.

Children need to eat food from a variety of different food groups in order to ensure an adequate intake of these macro and micronutrients. A growing child's diet should be made up of around 55–60% of energy from carbohydrate (foods like bread, cereal, potatoes, pasta, rice, and fruit and vegetables), 15–20% of energy from protein, and the rest from fat. Don't worry too much about this; it is just a guideline. We are not expected to measure out a child's intake in calories, grams and percentages! Try to visualise the overall diet as a plate, a third with starchy carbohydrates, a third with fruit and vegetables, and the last third made up of meat, fish, eggs, beans and other non-dairy protein, milk and other dairy foods, with a small amount of foods high in sugar and fat. This is the 'eatwell' plate model from the UK Food Standards Agency, which shows the types and proportions of different food groups in a healthy balanced diet for anyone over the age of two.

2. Say No to Processed

Meals and snacks made from fresh, natural ingredients will generally provide a better balance of nutrients than most processed foods, which tend to be high in 'bad' fats, sugar and salt. We are bombarded by health claims on the packaging of processed foods, especially those targeted at children; it's a minefield out there and we, as time-pressured shoppers, can be easily fooled. Claims of 'low fat', 'low sugar', 'healthy' or 'natural' are often misleading. The food giants may lower either salt, sugar or fat, but you will usually find that the levels of the other two are increased accordingly, in order to make them taste appealing. Consider, for instance, 'low-fat' biscuits and cakes, which are so often laden with sugar to make them more palatable.

Research suggests that children who are fed processed food from a young age can develop a strong taste for salt and sugar. Not surprising really, given the enormous sums of money invested by the food manufacturing industry to develop foods containing the perfect blend of salt, sugar and fats to create products that are irresistible.

Having said this, some snacks and ready-meals can be nutritious, but it takes careful examination of the ingredients to find these and, quite honestly, life's too short to waste time examining food packaging! It's time that could be much better spent preparing the equivalent at home.

A simple rule to follow is, if you don't recognise the ingredient in a product, then there's a good chance it's worth avoiding.

We can blame food giants and governments as much as we like for this, but ultimately it is we, as consumers, who make the choice. We don't have to buy the stuff.

The Eatwell Guide

Use the eatwell guide to help you get the balance right. It shows how much of what you eat should come from each food group.

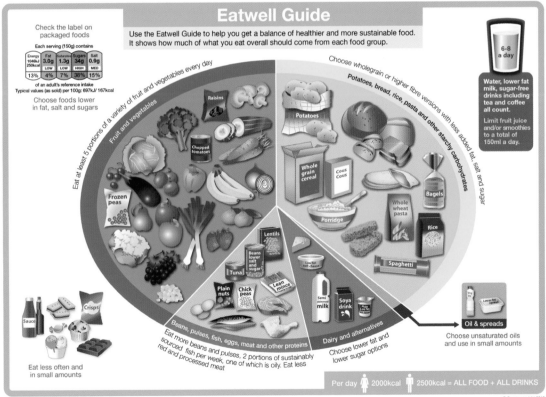

3. Cook from Scratch

This may require a little more planning, preparation and cooking time, but cooking from scratch, using fresh, natural ingredients means that you know exactly what you are fuelling your child with. You'll also save money and, most importantly, meals will generally taste much better!

4. Watch for 'Empty' Calories

Children who train regularly may need extra calories, but that's not an excuse to grab a bag of sugar-coated custard doughnuts on the way home from every competition or match. All foods provide energy (calories), but nutrient-rich calories will fuel a child's training and help prevent injury. They will also contribute to the development and growth of the body and, in turn, good long-term health and well-being. Doughnuts will contain calories, indeed they will contain lots of them, but the calories are 'empty', that is, poor in other essential nutrients. It's about quality not quantity!

"Would you put diesel into a Ferrari? NO!!"

The analogy of fuelling a car explains this clearly. Every car needs fuel. If a car starts a journey with a full tank, then it will go further. Furthermore, the finest and fastest cars need the finest quality fuel, and plenty of it. Similarly, an athlete who starts training with a full tank will be able to train for longer. Fuel that body with the best-quality fuel and this will 'supercharge' training. The athlete will exercise better, harder, for longer and with less of a chance of injury.

> " *My mum is a good cook and very interested in giving me and my brother the right nutrition. She makes Go Faster Date, Walnut and Apricot Flapjacks to fuel my training.*"
>
> Robert Poth, aged 15, GB Number 1 ski racer for age group, 2013.

5. Superfuel Training

Children need fuel to train efficiently. Consistent inadequate fuelling before exercise will result in low muscle stores and reduced endurance. This will increase the risk of fatigue, poor performance and possible injury. Timing is critical, however. There's no point cooking up a delicious spaghetti Bolognese if your child is off to swimming training thirty minutes later. At best that will make him or her feel sick, at worst, the pool may need to be drained! Best to offer a drink and an easily digestible snack, rich in slow-burning carbohydrate, to gradually release energy to the muscles. Save the spaghetti Bolognese for later...

6. Refuel for Recovery

Carbohydrate, the body's most efficient source of energy, is stored in the muscles and liver as glycogen. Glycogen levels become depleted after a workout and the quicker they are topped up again, the quicker children will recover, and, consequently, the better they will feel for the next session. Children will also need water and electrolytes to replace fluid loss, and protein to repair muscle cells. Encourage your child to rehydrate and eat something nutritious immediately after exercise (see hydration, pages 38–44).

7. Everything in Moderation

Children don't have to eat a perfect diet 100% of the time. Banning certain foods outright is usually asking for trouble. If a child adores cheesy crisps or a particular sugary cereal for instance, then denying access will just make him or her want them more. My younger son absolutely loves Thai chilli flavoured crisps, packed with salt and flavourings; of course he can have a bag of these for a treat every now and then, just not every day in his lunchbox! A little give and take makes everyone happier; eat well 80% of the time, relax a little for the remaining 20%.

8. Use your Judgement

There is no precise science as to how much an active child should eat. Children who are training for competitive sport need a higher intake of both macro and micronutrients to allow for the higher amount of energy expended. The exact amount will depend on each individual child's stage of development and include factors such as age, size and the level and type of activity (see daily energy requirements, page 36). An adolescent's demand for energy is pretty high compared with other age groups, even higher in the case of those who are training regularly. It is extremely important that adolescent athletes eat enough, both to fuel energy for their sport and to cope with the physical changes taking place as their bodies mature.

It is up to parents, carers or coaches to use their judgement here. For physically active children it is generally best to use appetite as a guideline. If a physically active child is still hungry having just eaten a meal, for instance, this probably means that he or she needs to eat more!

Signs that may indicate that a child is not eating enough to fuel his or her sport include:

- inability to recover properly between sessions
- lack of energy or feeling overly tired
- an increased susceptibility to colds and infections
- an inability to shake off these infections quickly

If you are concerned that a child is not eating enough, try monitoring how much they consume over the course of a week – it may add up to more than you reckoned. You may find that smaller frequent meals and snacks suit the child better than larger meals. This is definitely the case with my elder son, so I keep the fruit bowl topped up and leave healthy snacks, such as nuts, flapjacks or dried fruit, on the kitchen table for him to graze on.

If you are anxious about your child's eating, be vigilant for warning signs that could indicate the start of an eating problem. These include an obsession with weight or exercise, missing meals or cutting out certain food groups such as dairy, wheat or starchy carbohydrates. If this is the case, seek professional help from your general practitioner as soon as possible, especially if a whole food group is being avoided.

9. Adults as Role Models

Why should children lead a healthy lifestyle if the adults close to them are inactive and regularly tuck into beers and crisps in front of the TV? If children see those adults around them enjoying healthy food and working-out regularly, then they are more likely to do the same. This works especially well if these positive influences take place before children reach adolescence, after which they may be less inclined to hang on to an adult's every word!

" *We discuss balancing food groups and I guide Alice in her choices at home. We always sit at the table as a family for meals.*"

Mother of Alice Vyvyan-Robinson, aged 9, keen rugby player.

---

10. Involve the Kids

It takes time, effort and invariably causes a mess, but the more involved children are in the whole process of choosing food and preparing meals, the more likely they are to gain an awareness of different foods. They will learn why some foods are healthier than others and are more likely to enjoy the meals they have cooked themselves.

Shop for food together

Shopping together every now and then will help children appreciate the wealth of different foods available, the time and effort buying food takes and, with any luck, the size of the grocery bill. Send children to the shops on their own for a few basics. When children make a beeline for cleverly marketed packaged goods, which you may feel less inclined to buy, encourage them to read the nutritional information. That way, they can learn about salt, saturated fats and sugar, and perhaps find a healthier alternative.

Prepare food together

Involve children in planning meals and get them into the kitchen to help. If you can face it, let them loose on their own in the kitchen to create meals for themselves, or even for the whole family. All these efforts will contribute to a gradual awareness of different foods and why they are good (or not!) to eat.

Eat family meals together

Make this an integral part of everyday life. Research shows that children who eat family meals together are more likely to have a healthy attitude towards food. Enjoy the conviviality of eating good food together; start up an interesting conversation, try to relax, and children will enjoy their time at the table and be more inclined to try out new foods and dishes. Of course, this is not always practical, especially during the week when rushing from one activity to the other, but even one meal together once a week is better than nothing.

Matt Mason, aged 16, triathlete and skier, cooks his homemade burgers for his family

" *My family (Mum, Dad and 3 brothers) eat meals at the table every evening. I often come in around 9 o'clock so they have eaten, but they often sit with me.* "

Lucy Bryan, aged 17, Pole Vault, UK U20 outdoor record – 4.40m.

Encourage children to make informed choices

As children grow older they are bombarded by different food experiences and temptations, including school friends, role models, TV advertising, fast-food outlets and supermarket promotions. The earlier we can get children to understand about healthy eating and fuelling the body for their sport, the better, as they can then make their own sensible, informed choices, and with any luck, become the influencers rather than the influenced.

Essential Nutrients for Go Faster Kids

Count on Carbs

Carbohydrate-rich foods are the optimum fuel for energy and should form the bulk of an active child's diet. When children do sport, their muscles burn a combination of carbohydrate, protein and fat. The combination depends on the intensity and duration of the exercise. The longer and higher the intensity, the higher proportion of carbohydrate will be used. Carbohydrates, once digested, are eventually converted into blood glucose and used for energy, or stored in the liver and muscle. Glycogen stored in the liver is used to maintain steady blood glucose levels for the body and brain. Glycogen stored in the muscle is used to provide fuel for the muscles.

Children need to keep these glycogen stores topped up to prevent the body manufacturing glucose from muscle protein instead, as this will eventually lead to a loss of muscle mass.

Some carbohydrates are digested more rapidly into the bloodstream than others. This is excellent news for athletes, as they can consume different types of carbohydrates to fit in with their training goals. Carbohydrates that are digested slowly into the bloodstream are best consumed when sustained energy is required for endurance and stamina. Carbohydrates that are digested rapidly can be consumed to give short bursts of energy or to quickly replenish muscle glycogen stores after exercise to promote faster recovery.

Unrefined carbohydrates tend to provide more vitamins, minerals and fibre, or 'nutrient-rich' calories, than their more refined partners. Absorbed more steadily into the body, they will give children more stamina and help avoid dramatic sugar highs and lows. These are foods such as wholegrain bread, unprocessed cereals like whole rolled porridge oats, long-grain brown rice, wholewheat pasta, pulses and potatoes, fruit and vegetables.

Refined carbohydrates, found in processed or highly refined foods such as short-grain white rice, white bread, cakes, biscuits, confectionery and sugar, and sugary products such as fizzy drinks and sports drinks, are more rapidly absorbed by the body. They provide a quick blood sugar rush. This is great for during or immediately after exercise to replenish tired muscles, but not so good for keeping energy levels constant on a daily basis. Research shows that increased consumption of refined carbohydrates is one of the major causes of obesity.

The Glycaemic Index (GI)

In 1982, Dr David Jenkins, a professor in the Department of Nutritional Sciences at the University of Toronto, developed a method of classifying carbohydrates to indicate the speed at which they are digested and release sugars into the bloodstream. This is referred to as the Glycaemic Index (GI), in which carbohydrate-rich foods are given a rating between 0–100. A basic knowledge of the Glycaemic Index and how it works is extremely useful because the rate at which sugars are released into the bloodstream can have an enormous affect on a child's energy levels, and mental and physical performance.

When carbohydrates are consumed, a rise in blood glucose occurs and the body produces insulin. High-GI foods will cause a spike in insulin levels after meals, followed by a dramatic drop. The lower the GI level of a food, the slower and steadier the rise in blood glucose and, therefore, the more sustained the stream of energy. A diet with more low-GI foods may help reduce hunger pangs and energy slumps, maintain a healthy weight, and in turn, may lessen the risk of heart disease and type-2 diabetes.

Clever with Carbs

Using the Glycaemic Index, young athletes can manipulate their carbohydrate intake to suit their training goals by consuming the right type of carbohydrate at the appropriate time.

Low- and medium-GI carbs (GI of 70 and below)

A diet based on low- and medium-GI carbohydrates will ensure a much more stable level of blood glucose. The lower the GI, the more gradually the carbohydrate breaks down into the bloodstream and the slower the rate of digestion. This means that energy is supplied to the muscles more steadily, resulting in:

- fewer hunger pangs and cravings
- better stamina
- more sustained energy
- an improvement in concentration levels

High-GI carbs (GI of 70+)

The higher the GI, the faster the carbohydrate is absorbed and converted into blood glucose. Giving children high-GI snacks on a regular basis can teach the body to produce too much insulin, the hormone which transports carbohydrate into the liver and muscles. However, this does not mean that children should avoid high-GI carbohydrates entirely. Most parents will have experienced the effects of the 'sugar high' on children after drinking cola or eating ice cream or sweets. This can in fact be used to a child's advantage before and after sport. A high-GI snack just before or during sport can give muscles a rapid energy boost. Likewise, because the body resynthesises glycogen most efficiently straight after sport, the consumption of high-GI carbohydrates at this point will speed up muscle recovery. A quicker recovery will, in turn, enable the body to continue training on a consistent basis without injury or fatigue.

Foods and the Glycaemic Index

Low-GI foods – eat lots of these!

- Porridge
- Muesli (no sugar)
- Oat cereals
- High-fibre bran such as All-Bran™
- Spaghetti and most fresh and dried pasta
- Egg noodles
- Glass noodles
- Pumpernickel bread
- Granary/stone-ground wholemeal or sourdough bread
- Wholemeal pitta bread
- Pulses eg. lentils and chickpeas
- Beans eg. kidney, mung, soya, haricot, butter, blackeye, borlotti and baked beans

- Bulgur wheat, quinoa
- Most unsweetened dairy products – milk, cream, natural yoghurt, cottage cheese, hard cheese, ricotta etc
- Most fresh fruit – apples, pears, citrus fruits, bananas, figs, kiwis, mangoes
- Most non-starchy vegetables – aubergines, avocados, cabbage, broccoli, beansprouts, cauliflower, green beans, leafy greens, mushrooms, peas, sweetcorn, and salad vegetables such as lettuce, rocket, watercress, cucumber and tomatoes
- Dried apricots
- Nuts and seeds, peanut butter, tahini, hummus
- Fruit loaf
- Tea, milk drinks (no sugar)

Medium-GI foods – eat lots of these!

- Muesli (with sugar)
- Boiled potatoes with skin and sweet potatoes
- Wholewheat cereals, such as shredded wheat and Weetabix™
- Vegetables – beetroot and carrots
- Wholemeal bread, white pitta bread/most brown bread, rye bread
- Some fruit – fresh pineapple, melon, apricots

- Crumpets, oatcakes, digestive biscuits
- Tinned fruit
- Couscous
- Dried sultanas, raisins, prunes
- Basmati rice, dried rice noodles
- Muffins – bran, blueberry, banana
- Brown rice, risotto rice
- Honey, jam and marmalade

High-GI foods – eat less frequently or immediately after exercise

- Processed cereals such as bran flakes, corn flakes, puffed rice or wheat and sugary cereals
- Short-grain white rice
- Rice pudding
- White bread, baguette
- Bagels, rice cakes, crackers

- Potatoes – baked, fried, mashed – old potatoes have a higher GI than new (because of the type of starch)
- Some vegetables – broad beans, parsnips, pumpkin, swede, turnip, cassava
- Watermelon
- Dates

| *Top Tips* | **Carbs for Go Faster Kids** |

1. Base most meals on low- to medium-GI unrefined carbohydrates. Have fun experimenting with different types of wholegrain cereals, pasta, rice, couscous, quinoa, fruits and starchy vegetables.

2. Limit high-GI foods to immediately before or after exercise for that rapid glucose rush to feed the muscles.

3. A breakfast rich in low-GI carbohydrate plus a little protein will set children up for the day, resulting in increased concentration levels at school, better mood management and more sustained energy levels. Allow an extra 10 minutes to your morning schedule to sit down to breakfast. Set boundaries for this as you might do with other important daily undertakings, such as homework and teeth-cleaning, and explain the reasons why this is important. Healthy choices are wholegrain cereals*, porridge, granola with fruit and yoghurt, good-quality muesli or eggs on wholegrain toast. Use honey, agave syrup, dried fruit or bananas as sweeteners. Ditch the sugary, processed cereals, or limit these for immediately after an evening training session to promote good muscle recovery.

4. Snacks mid-morning, after school and before training should be packed with low-GI carbs. Try bananas, wholegrain sandwiches, flapjacks, baked beans, dried fruit, malt loaf, scones, teacakes, English muffins or crumpets.

5. Pulses and lentils are a great source of slow-burning carbohydrate. Put them in soups, make tasty snacks like falafel and hummus, add pulses, such as chickpeas and butter beans, to couscous dishes or stews.

*Offer bran-type foods to younger children in moderation. Too much fibre can prevent the absorption of some vitamins and minerals and may fill up their stomachs so that they are not hungry for other nutritious foods.

The Power of Protein

It is essential that children eat a certain amount of meat, fish or vegetarian alternatives such as eggs, cheese, milk, nuts, Quorn, beans or pulses to ensure that they get enough protein, as well as iron, zinc and B vitamins. Children's bodies are continually developing and growing so they need these foods, not only as a source of energy, but also for the health and development of their body tissues such as muscles, bones and red blood cells. Protein is also needed for making hormones and enzymes and for the immune system.

Active children will need slightly more protein than less active children, especially after an event or a heavy training session, to help repair damage to the muscles.

Try to include a couple of servings each day from the following selection:

- lean meat or poultry
- fish or shellfish
- eggs
- milk, yoghurt or cheese
- Quorn
- pulses or beans, such as lentils, baked beans, soya or soya bean curd (tofu) – great alternatives for vegetarians
- nuts and seeds
- grains, such as wheat (found in cereals, pasta and bread), rice and maize – these also provide some protein

Extra protein for muscle mass?

Those children wishing to gain muscle mass, for rugby, for instance, will need to consume calories in the form of carbohydrate, protein and fat to build muscle, in addition to the calories required to provide the energy required for regular training and matches. Boost protein intake with protein-rich snacks between meals, such as Greek yoghurt with honey, boiled eggs, peanut butter or cheese sandwiches. It is worth noting that the body can only absorb a certain amount of protein in any one sitting (about 4 grams per kg of body weight). It is not possible to build up stores of protein in the way that you can with carbohydrate; the body simply does not store it. If you overload on protein the excess will be excreted, putting an extra strain on the kidneys, or converted into fat rather than help build muscle. A child who wishes to gain muscle mass will need a good intake of protein each day of around 1.2 to 1.4 grams per kilo of body weight but this will need to be combined with a well-designed and sensible resistance training programme.

To put this into context, a physically active child weighing 50kg should eat 60–70g of protein per day. A can of tuna contains 40g of protein, a large glass of milk 16g, a small can of baked beans 10g, a lean (6oz) steak or salmon fillet 30g, and a small pot of yoghurt 6g. So, non-vegetarians can pack in enough protein without trying very hard.

Vegetarians will need to eat a good variety of milk, yoghurt, eggs, lentils, pulses, nuts and seeds and cereals to ensure they get a good balance of amino acids (the building blocks of protein). 'Protein complementation', that is, combining different vegetable proteins (beans and grains, for instance), is an efficient way to ensure that vegetarians consume the whole spectrum of amino acids that are essential for the body. For example, beans on toast, a handful of almonds and a glass of milk.

Timing of protein can help muscles

Protein taken in combination with quickly digestible carbohydrate before and during exercise will reduce muscle damage and delay loss of muscle strength. Protein consumed immediately after a workout will promote muscle recovery, growth and repair.

What about protein supplements?

My 17-year-old is concerned that he should bulk up to secure his position as flanker in his school 1st XV. A little 'on the skinny side', he's still growing and hasn't filled out yet. If he could 'beef up' he would avoid getting crushed in the rugby pack. Pressure on boys at this age to have the perfect six-pack and muscle-bound body is high. Cleverly marketed protein shakes and supplements are very tempting to young lads, but they are not only costly, they can interfere with the natural growth process and are, frankly,

unnecessary. Children can get enough protein from real foods. Protein supplements, such as whey protein shakes should only be taken by young athletes within the parameters of a balanced diet, for instance as an easily digestible and practical solution for during and post workout. Read the long list of bizarre ingredients and additives on many of these commercial protein supplements and you'll understand why! A cheaper, more natural and certainly more delicious option is to make your own protein-rich Go Faster Banana Recovery Shake (see page 206).

The more heavy-duty supplements, such as creatine, need to be used accurately and most certainly under professional guidance. Creatine builds muscle by dragging water into the cells which stimulates protein synthesis. Improper use of this can lead to dehydration, water retention, cramping, as well as kidney and muscle damage.

Top Tips | Protein for Go Faster Kids

1. Growing children should eat 2–3 portions of protein per day. Good choices are poultry, fish, eggs, beans or lentils. A little protein with all meals will slow the rate of digestion and so sustain energy levels better.

2. After training, healthy high-energy protein snacks combined with some carbohydrate, such as peanut butter sandwiches, baked beans on toast, cereal with milk or yoghurt, apple and cheese or poached eggs on toast, will help muscle health, growth and repair.

3. Boiled, poached, scrambled, even fried eggs are a fabulous and fast convenience food for athletes. Cheap, packed with protein and rich in essential vitamins and minerals such as iron, just one egg provides around 68 calories and around 13% of a child's daily protein.

4. Red meats such as lean steak, ham, duck breast, lean mince, and offal (including liver), are great sources of both protein and easily absorbed iron, especially important for teenage girls who train regularly. Oily fish such as sardines or pilchards as well as shellfish such as clams, mussels and scallops also contain both iron and protein.

5. Protein-rich vegetarian options, such as lentils and pulses, contain plant versions of iron. This is less easily absorbed, so offer vitamin C in the form of fruit juice, tomatoes or a green vegetable, such as broccoli, with these foods as this will help the body absorb the iron. To increase the protein intake of young vegetarian athletes, offer nuts and seeds as snacks or sprinkle them onto iron-fortified breakfast cereals, salads or couscous. Add pulses such as lentils to soups and stews.

Go
Faster
Kids

Lucy Bryan, aged 17

Pole Vault, PB 4.40m, UK U20 outdoor record, UK U17 all-time record, UKSG 1st place and record, 2010/2011, World Youth Bronze Medal 2011, Schools International Gold Medal and Record 2010

Bristol and West AC England and Great Britain Youth and Senior Teams

How often do you train?

After school, I train 6 times a week, a total of 11½ hours; I have Friday and Sunday off, but do two sessions on a Thursday, 3–4.30pm, then 6–8pm. I've just stopped my Wednesday session temporarily to concentrate on my A Levels.

What about competitions?

Competitions are either on a Saturday or Sunday during competition time. The indoor season is December to March, the outdoor season, May to August.

Your long-term ambition?

My immediate goal is to compete for the Great Britain Junior Team at the European Juniors in Rieti, Italy, then in the Olympics, hopefully Rio 2016 and the Commonwealth Games 2014. I want to make my parents and everyone else who has supported me proud!

What about your diet?

I've learnt about healthy eating through studying PE and Biology at school, and I get a lot of help from my Strength and Conditioning coach on what to eat before/after training and competition. I think I'm very controlled in what I eat and don't eat. I try to eat lots of protein as my sport is very power-based.

Ever too nervous to eat?

Never! I am always able to eat! I think when I am nervous I actually want to eat more.

Are you a breakfast person?

Yes! I usually have 2 scrambled eggs and a piece of toast.

What do you like to eat before training?

A small snack, perhaps a yoghurt and a small piece of fruit.

What's your favourite meal the night before a competition?

Lasagne and salad because it's a very well balanced meal.

What do you eat during tournaments?

Food is usually provided at tournaments, but if I were to take food, I would take a natural oat flapjack.

Do you drink commercial energy drinks?

I drink a chocolate flavour protein shake after strength and conditioning sessions, but I don't really drink energy drinks during training and competition, just water.

Friendly Fats for Fitness

Fat is an important nutrient for children. Children need to eat some fat to:

- provide essential fatty acids for healthy growth and development
- fuel the muscles
- transport vitamins and proteins around the body
- carry fat-soluble vitamins, such as vitamins A, D, E and K
- promote healthy skin and nerve function
- manufacture important hormones

Getting the balance right is the hard part! Children should be getting around 30% of their daily calories from fats, the majority of which should be from unsaturated fats rather than saturated. One cause of high LDL cholesterol (otherwise known as 'bad' cholesterol) is a diet high in saturated fat. LDL cholesterol can cause blood vessels to become narrowed or blocked and therefore can increase the risk of cardiovascular disease. Encouraging children to replace saturated fats with unsaturated will stand them in good stead for the future.

Unfriendly 'saturated' fats

According to UK government guidelines, saturated fat should make up less than 11% of a child's daily calorie intake. But what is saturated fat? It is the fat found mostly in animal and dairy products; the juicy bit of fat on steak, the crackling on your roast pork, the fat in processed meats, butter, cream, full-fat milk and cheese. Hydrogenated vegetable oils (often known as trans fats), found in some processed foods and takeaways, pastry, cakes and biscuits, also act like saturated fats in the body. Saturated fats will usually be hard at room temperature, whereas oils from unsaturated fats tend to stay liquid.

Foods high in unhealthy fat

- × fatty cuts of meat and meat products such as sausages and pies
- × butter, ghee and lard
- × cream, soured cream, crème fraîche and ice cream
- × cheese
- × cakes, biscuits and pastries made with butter, lard or hydrogenated vegetable oils or trans fats
- × savoury snacks, such as sausage rolls and pork pies
- × some sweet snacks and milk chocolate
- × palm oil

© Amilevin | Dreamstime.com

Friendly 'unsaturated' fats

Generally found in plant rather than animal products, unsaturated fats are vital for a child's healthy growth and development, and should make up around 20% of a child's daily calorie intake. Polyunsaturated fats provide 'essential fats' or EFAs (omega-3s and omega-6s) and are found in nuts and seeds, cold-pressed vegetable oils, such as sunflower, soya and corn and margarines made from them, as well as oily fish and avocados. Monounsaturated fats come from foods such as rapeseed, olives, some nuts and avocados. Both types of unsaturated fats can reduce the risk of cardiovascular disease, and may even play a role in improving immunity levels, mood, brain power and brain development. Recent studies have also hinted that a diet rich in EFAs can enhance sports performance.

Foods high in healthy fat

- ✓ avocados
- ✓ oily fish (tinned, smoked or fresh): salmon, sardines, mackerel, pilchards
- ✓ cold-pressed vegetable oils: sunflower, soya, safflower, olive, rapeseed, walnut, sesame, pumpkin seed, corn oil
- ✓ nuts and seeds
- ✓ nut butters: peanut or almond butter

Top Tips   **Fats for Go Faster Kids**

1. Do not cut saturated fat completely from a child's diet but encourage use in moderation. Spread butter moderately rather than in great chunks, or use a spread made from unsaturated fat. Use cream in moderation, trim the fat off fattier cuts of meat and avoid buying pastry-based processed meats such as pork pies and sausage rolls. Look for hidden saturated fat in biscuits, cakes and ready-meals.

2. Make a mental note to serve oily omega-3-rich fish at least twice a week. Buy fresh, smoked or tinned fish, such as mackerel, salmon, tuna, pilchards or sardines. Fresh fish can be expensive, so buy it for the freezer when it's on special offer, or buy frozen. Use it to make fish cakes, fish pie, grilled sardines or mackerel on toast, sardine or salmon pasta, pâtés or sandwiches. Note that tinned tuna, unlike the fresh variety, is quite low in omega-3.

3. Offer nuts and seeds as snacks and add them to meals. Roast your own nuts and seeds and leave them in a bowl in the kitchen for kids to snack on, or buy nuts in their shells – kids love to be let loose with the nutcrackers. Sprinkle sunflower and pumpkin seeds on cereal and into homemade granola. Use nuts in your cooking, for instance walnuts in salads, pine nuts on pasta, and pistachios with couscous.

4. Experiment with different healthy oils to use as alternatives to butter. For example, olive oil in mashed potatoes, walnut oil on steamed vegetables, or delicious pumpkin seed oil in salad dressings. Rapeseed oil, rich in omega-3 and vitamin E, heats to a high temperature without losing its nutrients to give excellent crispy results for frying; sunflower oil works well as an alternative to butter, giving very light results in some cakes and desserts.

5. Avocados are an excellent source of unsaturated fat and have a high calorific content. If you're lucky enough to have a child who'll eat them, then serve in salads, make spicy guacamole with crudités or add to sandwiches… Not one of my three kids likes avocados but they never seem to have a problem tucking into a spicy guacamole with warm pittas or nachos!

The imbalance of many teenagers' diets – high levels of saturated fat and low levels of vitamins and minerals – is a cause for concern. If you are worried that your child is eating too much saturated fat, try these following tips:

- Ditch the 'goodie cupboard'. Sounds a bit draconian, but this will trim both hips and grocery bill! A 'goodie cupboard' stocked with packaged snacks makes the introduction of healthy alternatives near on impossible. Restrict these to convenience on-the-go treats. Do this now and the habit will stick for life.

- Limit foods high in saturated fat, like sausages, pork pies, pasties, deep fried chicken etc.

- Use full-fat dairy products in moderation or swap for half-fat options; they're as high in protein and calcium.

- Make your own cakes, muffins and biscuits; you'll know what's in them and they'll taste better than the bought variety… usually! When buying ready-made, look for hidden saturated fats and sugar.

- Keep to regular meals based on starchy wholegrain foods, plenty of vegetables, plus fruit for dessert. This will reduce the desire to snack on fatty foods.

Vitamins and Minerals

Physically active children may need slightly higher amounts of vitamins and minerals than their less active friends. This is because regular and intensive training demands extra nutrients for efficient muscle function, cell repair and red blood cell formation. A broad spectrum of vitamins and minerals is required by the body in tiny amounts to provide the necessary nutrients for the body to function at its optimum. The wider variety of foods a child eats, the better chance he or she has to provide the body with all of these vital nutrients, which:

- help release energy from foods by enabling the body to use carbohydrate, fat and protein efficiently
- protect the immune system, the nervous system and the brain
- protect the health of teeth, bones, skin, eyesight, blood (basically everything!)

Fruit and Veg

Fruit and vegetables are particularly rich in essential vitamins and minerals, as well as other health-boosting phytochemicals. If you find it a struggle to get your kids to eat these, then you can rest in the knowledge that you're not alone! In fact, recent UK government figures* have revealed that only 13% of boys and 7% of girls aged 11–18 eat the recommended intake of five portions of fruit and vegetables per day. In a survey commissioned by the Cancer Research Campaign in 2011 which studied the eating habits of 2,635 11 to 16-year-olds in over 100 schools in England and Wales, it was found that almost 6%, that's around 200,000 children, had not eaten any fresh fruit or vegetables in seven days!

(ref. * The National Diet and Nutrition Survey (NDNS) is a continuous cross-sectional survey of the food consumption, nutrient intakes and nutritional status of the general population aged 18 months upwards living in private households in the UK. It covers all four countries of the UK and is designed to be representative of the UK population.)

Top Tips Fruit and veg for Go Faster Kids

1. Serve a choice of vegetables or salad with every meal; the more variety there is, the more likely there will be something children will choose.

2. Fruit and veg can be exciting; let the kids loose with the liquidiser to invent their own juices and smoothies, make interesting fresh salsas with, for instance, avocado, cucumber and mango, and introduce kids to delicious fresh herbs in your cooking.

3. Offer fresh fruit at breakfast every day; a spoonful of fruit salad, a small handful of blueberries, grapes or raspberries, ½ a grapefruit. Keep the fruit bowl topped up and store packs of berries in your freezer for smoothies.

4. Make quick, healthy soups using nutrient-rich vegetables, for instance, watercress, spinach, pumpkin, butternut squash or carrot.

5. Use fruit and veg in desserts; fruit crumbles, banana cake, carrot cake, courgette cake, apple cake, blueberry muffins.

6. Keep cooking to a minimum, as overcooking can reduce a vegetable's nutrient content; steaming, microwaving and stir-frying are good choices.

7. Send kids to school with raw fruit and veg as snacks; a nice crunchy carrot or apple, grapes or cherry tomatoes, for instance.

8. Subtle placing of chopped vegetables or fruit works wonders when children are at their hungriest, especially if accompanied by a tasty dip such as hummus; place a small plate in front of the television/computer after school or on the desk while they do their homework. Some kids are happy with frozen peas or even frozen grapes; pour them into a small bowl for them to pick at just as they may do a pack of sweets.

9. Non-vegetarians can try a meat-free day once a week; cook an oriental vegetable stir-fry, a potato and spinach or dhal curry, chilli 'sin' carne or butternut squash risotto.

10. Hide vegetables in food (sneaky, but highly effective!); grate apples, courgettes, mushrooms and carrots into stews, curries and Bolognese sauce.

11. If you are unsure whether your child is eating enough fruit and veg, aim for the government recommendation of 'five a day'. One portion for a child is roughly what will fit into a child's hand; a banana, a handful of peas or a satsuma for instance. A glass of fruit juice counts as one portion, a smoothie a maximum of two. Don't forget frozen and canned fruit and veg can also count. Dried fruit, as well as pulses and beans such as kidney beans, chickpeas and lentils, will also count, but only as one of the 5 a day.

"I love to make a fruit smoothie with bananas and strawberries for my breakfast."

Izzi Norman, aged 15, trains 7 times a week, county basketball player (Avon). Also likes to play netball, hockey, rounders, athletics and canoe polo "to keep fit and have fun!"

Fussy eaters?

There is unfortunately no magic answer to how to encourage children to eat a wide variety of different foods, in particular more fruit and vegetables. Children are individuals with minds of their own; many can be extremely headstrong! What works for one child doesn't always work for another. My two sons have always eaten large amounts of anything and everything, even as babies. My daughter, always happy to eat everything given to her as a baby, suddenly developed into a fussy toddler, and this continued for several years. Happy with protein and carbs – meat, fish, eggs and pasta were always high on the agenda – she would refuse to eat any vegetables, save a few frozen peas. By offering her plates containing a mix of foods she loved and new foods and never offering her an alternative, she

Come on sweetie, you know the rule: You need to finish your chocolate cake before you can have your carrots...

gradually started to eat more fruit and vegetables. I would even go as far as scraping the crumble off the top of an apple crumble for her, increasing the amount of apple each time. Aged 19, she is now an avid vegetable eater, so much so that when she returns home from college the first foods she asks for are spinach and Savoy cabbage!

Top Tips | For fussy eaters

1. Don't give up, keep offering small amounts of whatever you are serving.

2. Introduce different types and colours of fruit and vegetables on a gradual basis; a sort of drip-feed effect. If they are not keen on one item, don't fret too much, try offering it again a couple of weeks later.

3. Don't make a big issue out of it if food remains untouched.

4. Be a good role model yourself.

5. Refrain from offering alternatives (within reason).

6. Eat as a family as much as possible.

7. Make children clear the table; with any luck seeing what goes in the bin might play on their conscience.

8. Talk about the benefits of a balanced diet packed with vitamins and minerals; spot-free skin, glossy hair, improved brainpower, tip-top health for enhanced sports performance.

9. Take the kids shopping; they might pick out something they, or even you, have never tried before.

10. Involve children in cooking; ask them to peel and chop, stir sauces, taste for seasoning.

11. Encourage children to plan and cook complete meals for you (trying only to interfere when asked!). Get them thinking about what might be in a balanced meal.

Go Faster
Kids

© Constellation Media

Bertie Scoble, aged 14

Rugby, Bristol Academy EPDG Silver Group for U15's (Elite Player Development Group), Captain of age group for school and Old Bristolians RFC

Eventing, Banwell Pony Club and South West Area County Team

How often do you train?

Twice a week at school, every day after school and on Saturdays and Sundays.

What about matches and competitions?

In the winter I have 2–3 rugby matches a week at school, club or county level. Eventing competitions are on one evening in the week and over the whole weekend.

Do you have a long-term ambition?

I want to play professional rugby and represent England at international level. I love to keep fit, I love all my sports, and I want to achieve my best as an individual.

How much do you know about eating for better performance?

My rugby club, Old Bristolians, has taught me about hydration and it really works. The school has also provided good information, but there is a 'no-veg' option at lunch, which is wrong.

Do you eat healthily?

My family has a healthy diet and we normally eat together at the table, except at weekends, when we might sit in front of the telly for a treat. My mum always cooks at least two veg or salad with every meal, and I love to cook too; I've entered my school's Young Master Chef competition.

Breakfast: sugary cereal or porridge?

Actually, I'd be happy with toast, but I eat porridge with raisins or bran flakes with raisins on sports days (which is most days).

Do you ever suffer from pre-match nerves?

Yes, I don't like to eat before training as it makes me feel sick, so I normally eat after training.

What do you like to eat the night before a match or competition?

Steak with pasta and veg, followed by a yoghurt.

Do you have a favourite post-training meal?

Pasta bake with broccoli and tomatoes, or fish. I like Sundays best because we have a roast dinner in the evening with roast potatoes and Yorkshire puddings followed by a pudding!

Do you take food with you to tournaments?

Sandwiches, fruit and lots of squash, water and sometimes an energy drink.

Superfoods for Go Faster Kids

Beyond the basic nutrients of protein, fat, carbohydrate, fibre, vitamins and minerals, another group of chemicals called phytochemicals (plant-derived nutrients) is important for good health. Phytochemicals are usually related to the colour of the food, hence the term 'rainbow foods', with different colours containing different nutrients. For instance, lycopene in tomatoes, carotenoids in yellow, orange and red fruit and vegetables, and flavonoids in blueberries. Phytochemicals have health-boosting properties that support the immune system, help prevent diseases such as heart disease and cancer, and contribute to the metabolic processes that actually produce energy. The brilliant thing about these superfoods is that they are both healthy and exceedingly delicious; really worth encouraging children to eat. Contrary to popular belief, these foods don't have to be expensive.

Many basic fruits and vegetables, seeds, nuts, pulses and wholegrains can be reasonably classed as superfoods. Of course, no food is 'super' unless it is eaten as part of a balanced and varied diet. Overdosing on blueberries, for instance, will defeat the object (and bankrupt you) as the body can only absorb and store a certain amount of each nutrient. However, incorporating a rainbow of t hese different-coloured superfoods into a balanced diet is fun and will certainly help promote an interest in healthy eating.

A Rainbow of Superfoods

Colour Group	Fruit and Vegetables	Phytochemicals	Function
Red	Tomatoes Tomato sauce Tomato soup Watermelon	Lycopene Vitamin E	Helps control high blood pressure; reduces risk of cancers and cardiovascular disease
	Strawberries Raspberries Red apples	Anthocyanins	Powerful antioxidants; reduces risk of cancer and diabetes
Green	Broccoli Brussels sprouts Bok choy Cauliflower Cabbage	Indoles	Reduces risk of cancers
Green/Yellow	Spinach and greens Avocados Kale Green beans Green peppers Kiwis	Lutein	Helps maintain healthy vision
Orange	Carrots, sweet potatoes Pumpkins Butternut squash Mangoes Apricots Cantaloupe melon	Alpha and Beta-carotene	Antioxidants; reduces risk of cancers and cardiovascular disease; anti-inflammatory and supports immune system
Orange/Yellow	Oranges, orange juice Tangerines Yellow grapefruit Peaches Lemons, limes Papayas Pineapples Nectarines	Flavenoids Vitamin C	Helps maintain good vision, teeth, bones and healthy skin; powerful antioxidants; vitamin C for good muscle repair, iron absorption and to boost immune system
Red/Purple	Grapes, grape juice Cherries, blueberries Blackberries, strawberries Raspberries, cranberries	Anthocyanins Ellagic acid Flavenoids	Antioxidants; reduces risk of cancers, Alzheimer's and diabetes.
	Plums, prunes, raisins Aubergines	Phelonics	Powerful antioxidants; said to slow effects of aging
White/Green	Garlic Chives Onions, spring onions Leeks	Allicin	Helps lower blood pressure and high cholesterol; reduces risk of cardiovascular disease and cancer

Iron and Calcium

Some young people, particularly picky eaters and adolescents who are involved in intensive or competitive sport, will require additional energy and other nutrients in their diets. Low levels of calcium and iron are particularly common in female athletes, especially if they are restricting their food intake to maintain a low body weight (for instance, gymnasts, long-distance runners, lightweight rowers). This can have a serious effect on bone health and menstruation.

Iron

Iron is needed for healthy red blood cells which carry oxygen around the body. Low intakes lead to anaemia. Young female adolescent athletes have higher iron requirements, especially those who are training intensively. Meat, particularly red meat, liver, eggs and oily fish, are rich sources of well-absorbed iron. Plant foods, such as beans and pulses, green leafy vegetables, dried fruit (especially apricots), nuts and wholegrain cereals or fortified breakfast cereals with added vitamins also contain iron.

Symptoms of iron depletion can include lethargy, lack of appetite and susceptibility to colds and infections. If you suspect that your child may be lacking in iron, seek medical advice from your general practitioner before offering iron supplements. High doses of these can cause side effects.

Top Tips Iron for Go Faster Kids

1. Include plenty of these iron-rich foods on a regular basis:

   - iron-fortified cereals

   - lean red meat and poultry (the dark meat), liver

   - green, leafy vegetables, such as kale and watercress

   - nuts and dried fruit, especially apricots

   - cocoa powder, dark chocolate

   - wholegrains, such as brown rice, quinoa

   - beans

   - eggs

2. Iron is better absorbed from haeme (meat) rather than non-haeme (plant) sources, which contain fibre and substances called phytates and tannins. These bind the iron into compounds, making it harder for the body to get at. Eating plant sources of iron with foods that are rich in vitamin C (such as green leafy vegetables, tomatoes or fruit juice) can enhance the absorption. Tea and coffee will inhibit absorption so avoid drinking these at the same time as a meal.

Calcium

Children taking regular exercise need to make sure they are getting enough calcium. Milk and dairy foods provide this, along with the added bonuses of protein, vitamins A and B12 and riboflavin (which helps release energy from carbohydrates); all important for the health of our bones, skin and blood.

Top Tips — Calcium for Go Faster Kids

1. Encourage children to have 2–3 servings of milk, cheese or yoghurt every day. A serving is a glass of milk or a carton of yoghurt or a matchbox-sized piece of cheese.

2. Genuine milk allergy is relatively rare and often outgrown when children get older, but if your child cannot tolerate milk they will need a calcium-fortified milk alternative, such as soya milk or yoghurt, rice milk or almond-based milk products. Check the label for added calcium.

3. If your child doesn't like milk, offer yoghurt, drinking yoghurt, calcium-fortified soya milk or other non-dairy alternative, or tempt them with hot chocolate drinks, custard, rice pudding or milky desserts.

4. Offer milk at mealtimes and as a post-exercise recovery drink. A glass of milk, a milk shake or milk-based fruit smoothie makes an excellent post-exercise recovery drink, providing hydration along with a good balance of carbohydrate, protein and fat, plus vitamins and essential minerals such as calcium and potassium.

5. Include dairy foods in cooking; Parmesan cheese in risottos, pasta and salads; grilled haloumi cheese with a sweet chilli sauce (always a hit, even with non-cheese lovers). Use natural yoghurt and fromage frais in sauces and dressings.

6. Serve yoghurt or fromage frais regularly as a dessert. Some child-orientated products on the market have infuriatingly high sugar content, so check the label or buy the natural varieties (much more economical) and let children create their own concoctions with fruit, granola, honey or maple syrup and chocolate sprinkles. Adding your own means you can see exactly how much goes in. Likewise, buy regular cheese (cheddar, for instance) rather than processed products such as cheese strings.

7. Other good sources of calcium include:

   - tinned oily fish where you eat the bones, such as pilchards, sardines, mackerel and salmon

   - some leafy green vegetables, such as spinach, broccoli, spring greens or kale (also rich in magnesium and vitamin K which help build strong bones)

   - pumpkin, sunflower and sesame seeds, Brazil nuts and almonds

   - pulses, beans and tofu

   - bread

   - dried fruit such as figs and apricots

Salt

We all need a certain amount of salt in our diet to keep our body fluids at the correct concentration. Most of us, however, eat more than we need. Too much salt in our diet increases the volume of body fluids and pushes up blood pressure, which can lead to serious problems such as heart disease and stroke. The maximum recommended intake of salt for adults and children over 11 years is 6g per day, children aged 7–10 should have no more than 5g per day. Some foods, such as crisps and bacon, taste obviously salty and so are easy to detect, but salt is often hidden in foods. In fact, according to the NHS, 75% of the salt we eat comes from ready-made staples such as bread, cereals, baked beans and even biscuits.

Daily Nutrient Requirements for Children

The energy and nutrient requirements for children are shown below according to age and sex. Children who are training for competitive sport will have a higher requirement to allow for the higher amount of energy expended. The actual amount will of course vary according to the individual child's stage of development and the level and type of activity.

Daily energy and nutrient requirements for 7 to 10-year-olds

Sex	Energy (EAR)*	Protein (RNI)**	Calcium (RNI)	Iron (RNI)	Total Fat	Sat Fat	Salt
Boys	1,970 cals	28.3g	550mg	8.7mg	76.6g	24.1g	5g
Girls	1,740 cals	28.3g	550mg	8.7mg	67.6g	21.3g	5g

Daily energy and nutrient requirements for 11 to 14-year-olds

Sex	Energy (EAR)*	Protein (RNI)**	Calcium (RNI)	Iron (RNI)	Total Fat	Sat Fat	Salt
Boys	2,220 cals	42.1g	1,000mg	11.3mg	86.3g	27.1g	6g
Girls	1,845 cals	41.2g	800mg	14.8mg	71.6g	22.6g	6g

Daily energy and nutrient requirements for 15 to 18-year-olds

Sex	Energy (EAR)*	Protein (RNI)**	Calcium (RNI)	Iron (RNI)	Total Fat	Sat Fat	Salt
Boys	2,775 cals	55.2g	1,000mg	11.3mg	107.1g	33.7g	6g
Girls	2,110 cals	45g	800mg	14.8mg	82.1g	25.8g	6g

*EAR - Estimated Average Requirement
**RNI - Reference Nutrient Intake
Taken from the Government's Committee on the Medical Aspects of Food Policy (1991) Dietary Reference Values for Food Energy and Nutrients for the UK Report no.41. London HMSO

Alice Vyvyan-Robinson, aged 9

All-rounder: athletics, cricket, football, hockey, netball, rounders, rugby, skiing, surfing and swimming

School 'A' teams and club rugby, football and hockey

How often do you do sport?

I train 6 times a week at school, 3 times a week after school and I have 3 training sessions at weekends. We have matches almost every week and most weekends, sometimes even two mid-week and two weekend matches.

Do you have a favourite sport?

I love all sport, but my favourites are rugby, hockey, athletics, skiing and surfing.

What is your main motivation?

I love to win! I go out with all my might and determination when I play, and I like to try out all the skills I have learnt in training.

Do you eat healthily?

Yes, I like my food and my Mum has told me about balancing food groups. She also makes me think about whether I am eating because I am hungry or whether I am just being greedy!

Do you ever find it difficult to eat?

Yes, after matches my tummy feels all 'mixed up' and takes time to settle down.

What do you like to eat before training?

If training is after breakfast, I'll eat fruit and yoghurt, if training is later, I eat pasta.

What's your favourite meal the night before a match?

Spag Bol and peas followed by homemade chocolate chip cake and fruit.

What do you eat during tournaments?

Bananas, apples and chocolate bars. During cold rugby tournaments, I drink hot chocolate, otherwise I drink water.

Hydration for Go Faster Kids

Around two-thirds of our body weight is water. We need water and other fluids for our bodies to function properly and to prevent dehydration. Most of the chemical reactions that occur in our cells need water. We need it to enable our blood to carry nutrients around the body and get rid of waste, and we need water for hydration. Good hydration is key for children who want to perform to their best ability, both mentally and physically. Children are at more risk of dehydration than adults for several reasons:

1. Children have immature thirst mechanisms and can find it difficult to recognise when they are thirsty or just forget to drink!

2. Children have a higher surface area to body mass ratio compared to adults. This means that they are more likely to lose water by evaporation and are therefore more at risk of dehydration.

3. The kidneys play a vital role in regulating the amount of fluid in the body. Children have less developed sweating and kidney functions, which means that they are more likely than adults to become dehydrated in hot weather or during intense physical exercise.

How much should an active child drink?

There is no 'one size fits all' rule to good hydration. Firstly, each individual sweats at a different rate, according to age, size and sex. Secondly, the composition of each person's sweat is individual. External factors such as the temperature, humidity, the type and the intensity and duration of the exercise also play a part.

© zenwae | Dreamstime.com

The British Nutrition Foundation recommends that children and adults should drink 6–8 glasses of fluid per day, preferably keeping fluid levels topped up throughout the course of the day. This does not have to be just water; fruit juice, milk, tea and coffee also count. Teenage boys, in particular, need more fluid than girls. In the UK, there are no agreed recommended daily intake levels specifically for teenagers, but recommendations from the US National Academies Food and Nutrition Board suggest that 9 to 13-year-old girls should drink 1.6 litres per day and boys should drink 1.8 litres per day; 14 to 18-year-old girls should drink 1.8 litres per day and boys drink 2.6 litres per day. Active children, as with active adults, should drink in addition to this during hot weather and before, during and after physical activity.

Of course, children spend at least half of their waking hours in school, so it's important to encourage them to drink 3 or 4 of these glasses during the school day. Easier said than done, but worth the effort! Several studies* have shown that cognitive function, especially in terms of concentration and attention, is improved with good hydration throughout the day, and this has led to better provision of drinking water in many schools in both the US and the UK.

How can I tell if my child is drinking enough?

Children can check their hydration levels by ensuring that they are producing plenty of pale, straw-coloured urine. The darker the urine, the less hydrated they will be, as you can see from the urine chart (right).

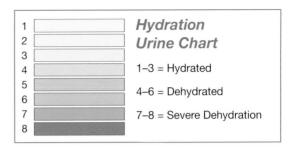

Symptoms of dehydration

When we sweat our blood volume decreases and there is less oxygen-rich blood available to the muscles. The muscles are being pushed to capacity yet are receiving fewer nutrients. This makes us slow down as the body fights to maintain its core temperature.

Even mild dehydration can have physiological consequences. As you can see from this graph, a simple loss of just 1% body weight can start to decrease performance (that's a mere 400ml for a

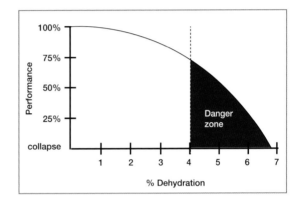

40kg child). A loss of 2% body weight can reduce performance by 10–20% in terms of both mental concentration and focus and physical stamina and co-ordination.

Potential Short-Term Effects of Dehydration

Physical symptoms	Mental symptoms
• Lack of energy or headaches	• Restlessness
• Light-headedness	• Irritability
• Nausea	• Reduced concentration
• Dark-coloured urine and not passing much when going to the toilet	• Confusion, feeling of disorientation
• Reduced muscular strength	• Lack of alertness and accuracy
• Impaired co-ordination	• Impaired decision-making ability
• Impaired physical endurance	• Impaired ability to do mental arithmetic
• Cramping	• Impaired short-term memory
• Shortness of breath	
• Reduced skin turgor – a 'lasting skinfold' when pinched	
• Constipation	

*i) Anci KE, Constant F and Rosenberg IH (2006) Hydration and Cognitive Function in Children, Nutrition Reviews 64: 457-464
ii) Edmonds CJ and Burford D (2009) Should children drink more water? The effects of drinking water on cognition in children.
   Appetite 52:776-9

© No050 | Dreamstime.com

What should active children drink to hydrate?

Water first

Children can get their fluid requirement from a number of sources including fruit juice, milk, smoothies and tea, although water should be the first choice for basic hydration. It is cheap, convenient, calorie-free and has no sugars that can damage teeth. Some foods can provide fluid as well as nutritional value; many fruits and vegetables contain as much as 80–90% water, for instance watermelon, cucumber, or vegetable soups. Even foods such as cooked pasta and potatoes are about 70% water.

Fizzy drinks

A mother of a 15-year-old boy recently asked me whether she should give her son sugar-free 'diet' or full-sugar fizzy drinks. 'Diet' or not, these drinks provide little or no nutritional value and can be damaging to the teeth. While high levels of sugar in drinks are a major cause of tooth decay in children, it is the acidity in fizzy drinks, both 'diet' and full-sugar, that causes tooth erosion, that is, the wearing away of the enamel coating on teeth. It's not just fizzy drinks that are the bad guys. Many soft drinks are packed with sugar. The figures speak for themselves; a 330ml can of cola contains the equivalent of 10 teaspoons of sugar, a standard 500ml bottle of some flavoured waters an unexpected 7 teaspoons of sugar. The recommended daily allowance of sugar for a 10-year-old is 9 teaspoons.

Energy and sports drinks

Packed with sugar, and sometimes energy-boosting stimulants, such as caffeine and guarana, energy and sports drinks are marketed to children and adolescents both as 'cool' and as a magic formula to optimise performance. In my world of marathon running, sports drinks are recommended when training intensively for over 90 minutes, to replenish depleted glycogen stores and replace electrolytes lost through sweat. It frustrates me to see children downing these expensive drinks on the way to school or before a standard training session. These drinks have a place for serious athletes doing longer training sessions of 90 minutes or more, or repeated bouts of exercise. However, children doing moderate exercise should not need the high levels of carbohydrate, protein, electrolytes and vitamins in a sports or energy drink; water and a healthy, balanced diet should suffice. Frequent or excessive intake of calorific sports drinks can substantially increase the risk of obesity in children and adolescents. It is a hard and often unwelcome lesson to learn, but these drinks will not perform miracles. Performance will only improve in the long-term through sheer hard work, patience and focus! A 2011 clinical study* on the ingredients of sports and energy drinks and the effect of these drinks on children and adolescents concluded that the use of sports drinks in place of water on sports fields or in school dining rooms is generally unnecessary, and that the use of energy drinks containing stimulants has no place in the diets of children and adolescents.

Hydration and exercise

Children involved in competitive endurance, repeated bursts of physical activity throughout the day, such as swimming or football tournaments or other prolonged vigorous physical activities need to keep hydration levels topped up, especially during hot weather, as they will invariably forget to drink, or not even experience thirst. As children start to sweat, the core body temperature increases. This causes a decrease in blood volume which is necessary for carrying blood to the heart. There is consequently less oxygen-rich blood available to fuel the working muscles. When it is really hot, the body tries to cool itself down by sending more blood to the capillaries of the skin, which further reduces the blood flow to the muscles. The body becomes increasingly dehydrated as it fights to maintain its core temperature and, consequently, performance and concentration decreases. As a guideline, children taking part in prolonged and vigorous physical activity need between 150ml and 250ml water about every 20 minutes, although this amount will vary according to weather conditions, intensity of activity and the age and weight of the child.

Prolonged physical activity

Sweat is salty; it can make your eyes sting and stain your clothes. It is, in fact, made up of water and a combination of minerals (sodium, potassium, chloride and magnesium) known as electrolytes. Electrolytes are necessary for the body to function properly. During periods of physical activity of over an hour, such as long-distance running or a high-intensity activity such as football, it may be beneficial for children to drink a sports drink. The minerals in the sports drink will replace those lost through sweat and the carbohydrate will replenish depleted energy glycogen stores. However, this doesn't have to be an expensive option; homemade sports drinks can be just as effective.

*American Academy of Pediatrics Committee on Nutrition (CON) and Council on Sports Medicine and Fitness (COSMF)(2011) Sports Drinks and Energy Drinks for Children and Adolescents: Are They Appropriate? Pediatrics, 127:1182-1189

Go Faster Kids

"*I used to drink commercial energy drinks, but now I drink just water; it's cheap, effective and really refreshing.*"

Phoebe Budd-Stone, aged 13, trains 5 times a week, county hockey player, Junior Regional Programme, Clifton Ladies U14 player of the year; Orienteering – winner of year group in Bristol Schools League.

Ambition: "To play hockey for England."

Recipes for homemade isotonic sports drinks:

Recipe 1

Measure out 250ml pure unsweetened fruit juice (any flavour)

Add 250ml water to make a total volume of 500ml

Add a pinch of salt (about 1/5 tsp)

Mix together and stir or shake well. Chill in the fridge.

Recipe 2

Measure out 100ml squash (any flavour, but full sugar)

Add 400ml water to make a total volume of 500ml

Add a pinch of salt (about 1/5 tsp)

Mix together and stir or shake well. Chill in the fridge.

" If I'm doing a particularly hard session and it's very hot, I sometimes take a bottle of homemade energy drink... normally my bottles are filled with only water."

Dan McKimm, aged 18, Road and Track Cyclist.

After exercise

Water will be sufficient to rehydrate after exercise, unless the workout has been for a prolonged period or the weather is extremely hot. If you are lucky enough to have a child who likes drinking milk, or chocolate milk, you will see from the table below that these make extremely effective recovery drinks, and can in fact be more effective than commercial sports drinks, providing:

- fluid and electrolytes for rehydration
- protein to help muscle recovery and growth
- carbohydrate to replenish depleted muscle glycogen stores

Nutrition per 250ml serving	Energy (kcal)	Sodium (mg)	Potassium (mg)	Protein (g)	Carbs (g)
Water	–	–	–	–	–
Average sports drink	50–70	110	25	–	14–16
Semi-skimmed milk	115	107	390	8.5	11.7
Chocolate milk	157	112	515	9	23.5
Homemade sports drink	50–55	135	190	<1	11–15
Orange juice	90	25	375	1.2	22

Top Tips Hydration for Go Faster Kids

1. Offer water and fluids with all meals.

2. Provide plenty to drink at breakfast as a routine, so kids go to school well-hydrated. Give them a bottle of water in the hope that they might drink it and top it up at a water fountain. Encourage children to drink water as soon as they return from school.

3. If you don't buy sugary drinks, then they won't be in the house to drink. Offer sugar-free squash as a good alternative if your child won't drink plain water.

4. Encourage children to drink plenty of water after exercise, or a sports drink after heavy, prolonged exercise. Don't forget milk or a calcium-enriched, non-dairy alternative makes a cheap and very effective post-exercise drink.

5. In hot weather and before and after exercise, offer hydrating snacks including melon, oranges, cucumber slices or red peppers. Also, provide nutritious snacks containing salt, such as breakfast cereal, a sandwich or toast with marmite or peanut butter, to replace salts lost through sweat.

Banana Recovery Shakes (see page 206)

Jake Norman, aged 15

Freestyle Kayaking, 12th place in ICF Kayak Freestyle World Championship 2013, K1 Junior Men

GB Team and North Avon Canoe Club

How often do you train?

I also play tennis, rugby and canoe polo, so in total I train twice a week at school, four times a week after school, then one or two 4-hour sessions at weekends.

How often do you compete?

There are 10 freestyle events and 2 canoe polo tournaments per year.

Any ambitions?

I want to achieve my best as an individual but my specific goal is to make Junior World Champion in 2015.

How about healthy eating?

I think I eat a healthy diet, although I haven't been given any information specific to my sport. I try to eat low-fat foods and slow-burning carbs when I'm training.

Do you feel pressure to be a particular body shape?

Yes, to some extent. I try to have a really good strength-to-weight ratio to help my freestyle performance.

Favourite training breakfast?

A bowl of porridge or Weetabix™ and fruit.

And post-training?

I love to eat lasagne after a hard training session.

What do you take to eat for tournaments?

I need a lot to keep me going so I take foods such as sandwiches, fruit, flapjacks, nuts, fruitcake and pasta.

Top Carbs for Go Faster Kids

Oats

Send the kids off to school with a bowl of hot porridge inside them and you'll be doing them a great favour. Packed with low-GI carbohydrate and plenty of protein, B vitamins, vitamin E, fibre and minerals, including iron and calcium from the milk, porridge oats make the ultimate fitness breakfast. Porridge will fill kids up, provide sustained energy, help concentration and minimise mid-morning starvation pangs. Regular consumption of oats can also help maintain a healthy digestive system and blood cholesterol levels.

For children who don't like porridge, try making homemade granola (see Crunchy Granola, page 67), delicious on its own with milk or yoghurt and honey, or sprinkled over cereal. Alternatively, try adding oats to a pancake mixture (see Apple Power Pancakes, page 78). Homemade flapjacks and energy bars are a far healthier option as an energy-boosting snack than commercial biscuits and chocolate bars.

Pasta

Wheat pasta, fresh or dried, makes a fabulous energy food. It is cheap and convenient too. In fact, it is far quicker to throw together a simple, nutritious pasta dish than queue, wait and pay for a fast-food meal. Pasta has a surprisingly low glycaemic index, releasing glucose gradually into the bloodstream and thus maintaining more stable blood sugar levels. It is low in fat and makes a fantastic staple to include in a child's everyday diet. Although most kids prefer the more refined white pasta, the brown wholewheat variety is more nutritious and sustaining than white, containing more fibre, minerals (including manganese, magnesium and iron), and B vitamins. Consider a compromise with one of the semi-wholewheat varieties now commonly available.

In times of panic and stress, I always resort to the old favourite – pasta with pesto, extra pine nuts and bacon pieces. The ultimate quick dish, equally good spooned into a plastic container as a packed lunch or on-the-go meal for a tournament as it is as a speedy and nutritious family meal.

Rice

Rice makes an excellent fuel for young athletes. Low in fat, rice is a rich source of B vitamins and a range of minerals. As with pasta, white rice has been refined, depleted of much of its bran, germ and goodness, so the less-refined brown varieties are far richer in nutrients.

Rice is classified according to the length of its grain. The longer the grain, the lower the GI and, therefore, the more sustaining.

Long-grain basmati, white or brown, has the lowest-GI factor. Delicious, fluffy and easy to prepare, this rice makes the best choice for everyday cooking.

Risotto rice, both medium in grain and in GI, makes a wonderful staple. Most kids like the creaminess of risottos and they make a perfect vehicle for using up leftovers, or whatever there might be lurking in the store cupboard or freezer. A 'summer' pea risotto made with frozen peas, for instance, or a 'leftovers' risotto using meat from the Sunday roast and tired vegetables from the veg rack.

Speciality rice varieties are often more nutrient-dense than the everyday varieties and are always worth a try with more adventurous children. Wild rice tastes great when mixed with brown basmati, and three-grain rice works well in a risotto. Spanish paella rice or red Camargue rice is delicious cooked with prawns or chicken. And black rice always goes down well at Halloween!

Short-grain rice, such as pudding rice or jasmine rice, has a high GI, and is best served with a post-match or workout meal, such as rice pudding or a Thai curry.

Rice noodles, or vermicelli, with a low GI, make a fabulous 'fast-food'. Pour boiling water onto a bunch of cellophane noodles, wait a few minutes, and use in stir-fries, salads and soups.

Couscous and Bulgur Wheat

Your luck's in if you have a child who likes any of these! Versatile, tasty, light on the stomach and a doddle to prepare, couscous and bulgur wheat provide sustaining and nutrient-dense carbohydrate for the young athlete.

Couscous is made from 100% durum wheat flour.
Add boiling water, a little salt, a splash of olive oil, perhaps a stock cube, wait 5 minutes and it's ready. Serve either warm as an accompaniment to a tagine, stew or kebab, or with roasted vegetables and spices, or cold, as Tabbouleh, with salad vegetables and heaps of fresh herbs.

Bulgur wheat can be used in the same way as couscous. I think it has a deliciously nutty flavour, but in my experience, kids tend to prefer the more refined couscous. Bulgur wheat takes marginally longer to cook, has a lower GI, and is all the more nutritious for it.

Quinoa

Gluten-free, wheat-free and packed with an astounding array of nutrients, quinoa provides an excellent level of slow-release energy. It works well as an alternative to pasta, couscous or rice and is both delicious and easy to digest. Quinoa contains a good range of amino acids, making it a good-quality protein, and has a high mineral content, including calcium, magnesium,

manganese, iron and potassium. Try it out on your kids. My boys tolerate it because they know my daughter and I love it, but would be happier with rice!

Polenta

Comfort food for a cold day, polenta, cooked 'wet' style, with a mushroom and prawn sauce, or simply with grated Parmesan, olive oil and black pepper, are two of my elder son's favourite pre-match lunches. Polenta certainly has sustained him through many wintery afternoons of rugby. Made from cornmeal, polenta has a smooth, creamy texture and is perfect for gluten- or wheat-free diets. It can be used in cakes and muffins, cooked as a soft 'wet' polenta, or cooked for a little longer and left to cool in a baking tray to be cut into slices and grilled or fried. Instant polenta takes literally one minute to cook and is almost as delicious as the real thing, especially eaten with a drizzle of extra virgin olive oil and shavings of Parmesan.

Potatoes

Potatoes are packed with nutritious goodness. Although high in carbohydrate, they are also rich in vitamin C and minerals such as potassium, as well as fibre. The glycaemic value of potatoes varies according to how they are cooked.

Mashed, baked and chipped potatoes have a high GI. This gives us a great excuse to eat them as part of a recovery meal after exercise to replenish depleted energy stores.

Gnocchi are little Italian dumplings made from potato and flour, bound together with egg. Once made, they are a fantastic fast food, taking only a few minutes to cook. They are delicious with a simple tomato or pesto sauce and, with a medium to high GI, are good to eat for recovery.

If you are feeling adventurous, you can make your own gnocchi; you'll find a gnocchi recipe in this book, but you can buy very good ready-made gnocchi in the supermarket.

New potatoes have the lowest GI, especially when boiled or steamed with their skins on.

Sweet potatoes make a tasty alternative to potatoes. Extremely high in antioxidants, and with a medium GI, they are an excellent source of vitamin A (beta-carotene), vitamin C, manganese, copper, fibre, potassium and iron, and are great for maintaining steady blood sugar levels.

Lentils and Pulses

Packed with slow-release, low-GI carbohydrate, protein, B vitamins, fibre and minerals such as calcium, iron and zinc, lentils and pulses are excellent for sustaining energy levels and boosting the immune system.

Lentils and pulses are delicious added to chilli con carne, soups, sauces, casseroles, rice and couscous. You can even blitz them in the food processor to disguise them if your children are less than keen, they won't notice they are eating them! Most children love hummus. Made with chickpeas or other beans if you like, it's incredibly easy to make at home, much cheaper and infinitely more delicious than supermarket hummus (see Hummus recipe, page 169).

Fruit and Starchy Vegetables

Fruit and starchy vegetables are super sources of carbohydrate, with the added benefit of being packed with important vitamins and minerals to support a healthy body and immune system. Fruits, such as cherries, apples, bananas, kiwis, pears, pineapples, mangoes, strawberries and grapes, and vegetables, such as beetroot, butternut squash, carrots, corn, peas, sweet potatoes and parsnips, are all a good source of nutrient-rich carbohydrate.

Go
Faster
Kids

" *I love to eat Go Faster's Smoky Black Bean and Chorizo Chilli! It's a great meal to fuel up on to help consistent back-to-back training!*"

Daniel McKimm, Road and Track Cyclist.

Daniel McKimm, aged 18

Cycling, Road and Track, ranked 5th in South Region and 33rd nationally, 2013
Career stats – wins: 4, podium: 12, top 10s: 46

Team Dream Cycling

Tell me about your team?

Dream Cycling is a semi-professional team which competes in regional, national and international events.

How often do you train?

Twice a week before school, twice a week after school as well as Saturdays and Sundays.

How often do you compete?

At least once a week from the end of February to the end of September; although between May and August I usually race twice a week.

What are your cycling ambitions?

I have a desire to compete and perform at the highest possible level. My main goal is to become a professional rider and, ideally, I'd like to make a living from the sport. I am consistently getting results in Elite races against full-time and professional riders.

Do you know much about eating for better performance?

I did some nutrition workshops through a Sport England programme a couple of years back.

What about your diet?

I try to eat foods and fluids that will give me the greatest nutritional benefit for what I need at a certain time (i.e. for energy, recovery etc), although it's nice to eat whatever you feel like once in a while! In the build up to a race, I always try to increase my intake of water to ensure I am suitably hydrated when I arrive at the start line. I also increase my carbohydrate intake in the days leading up to a race so that I've got enough fuel in the tank when I'm racing.

Favourite training breakfast?

A bowl of porridge with a good sprinkling of sugar or a dollop of stewed apple.

And post-ride?

I'll have a large bowl of oat granola with loads of milk and perhaps a slice of toast and marmalade for a bit of a sugar boost. If I've been for a long ride, I'll have beans on toast or chicken and pasta.

Favourite meal for the night before a race?

Go Faster's Smoky Black Bean and Chorizo Chilli! I love that stuff!

What do you take to eat on stage races?

It's essential to eat between stages so that I can recover from the first one and refuel sufficiently for the second. My usual tipple is a pasta pot with chicken or tuna, tomatoes and pesto or tomato sauce. I'll have a banana and a cereal bar too.

Putting Theory into Practice

Practical fuelling for Go Faster Kids

It's easy to talk the talk, not so easy to walk the walk! Good healthy eating intentions can often go awry in real life. Busy work schedules, family commitments, school work and before- and after-school training can get in the way of sitting down to freshly prepared meals every day. In the Go Faster Food house, regular weekly activities include a massive variety of sports and musical activities, with one or more things going on most evenings. Like many parents, weekends are spent taxiing to and fro between different sports fixtures, galas and athletics meets. Squeezing the purchasing, preparing and eating of nutritionally balanced meals into this whirlwind of family and work life is certainly a challenge. But it is possible!

1. Plan ahead. Think about how the week is going to pan out and buy appropriately. Try buying store cupboard goods online and then, depending on your daily schedule, shop on a frequent basis for small quantities of fresh ingredients.

2. Keep cupboards well-stocked with store cupboard items so that you can make meals and healthy snacks when you don't have time to shop.

3. Cook larger quantities of foods such as soups, stews and pasta sauces for the freezer.

4. Invest in a slow cooker so the work is done for you while you are out of the house.

The right foods at the right time for optimum performance

Organising the timing of meals and snacks according to children's training and competing can greatly enhance performance, reduce fatigue and minimise the risk of both injury and catching bugs and viruses. Children need calories before sport to provide the correct level of energy, during sport to sustain this energy and after sport to promote quick recovery.

Before training

The better fuelled young athletes are when they start a training session the longer and harder they will be able to exercise, and consequently the more benefit they will gain. Remember the Ferrari scenario? Starting exercise with a full tank of quality fuel will provide the energy and calories for better performance. If a child trains repeatedly on an empty stomach, or rather, with inadequate carbohydrate stores in the muscles, he or she will tire early, feel weak and find it difficult to keep up with his or her teammates; this will eventually lead to muscle loss and potential injury.

The ideal time to eat before exercise is around 2–4 hours for a main meal, or 1–2 hours for a snack, allowing just enough time for the body to digest the food. If you leave it too long, the average kid will most likely get hungry again, any closer to training, blood will be supplying the digestive process rather than the muscles and this can lead to nausea or stomach discomfort.

If there is enough time before training to digest a meal, then foods based on low- to medium-GI carbohydrates will feed energy gradually to the muscles to provide sustained energy. The addition of a little protein will effectively lower the GI of the overall meal, as well as contribute towards muscle health. The meal should not be too high in fat, as this takes longer to digest, so avoid offering fried foods and pastries, such as chips and sausage rolls. Good choices are porridge or muesli with milk, pasta with pesto or tomato sauce, or a tuna sandwich on wholemeal bread.

" I always eat before I train; bagels, muesli, yoghurt, fruit and nuts."

Fred Oldfield, aged 17, plays cricket, Millfield 1st Team and Gloucestershire U17s and county hockey, Avon.

Too close to training?

Of course, in practice, that perfect two-hour window is often hard to find! There is frequently very little time to eat a proper meal to fuel a training session. Sometimes, there's only a short gap between the end of school and the start of after-school training, or worse still, training is pre-school, so it's a challenge to eat a decent breakfast so early.

At these times, a small easily digestible high-carb snack, such as a flapjack, a banana, a breakfast bar (try Go Faster Breakfast Rock Cakes, page 81), a slice of toast with peanut butter or a handful of raisins, is more appropriate than a meal. If solids are not an option, then try a nutritious drink such as a mug of hot chocolate, milkshake or a smoothie. For those early mornings when your child cannot face eating anything, just a few bites of something and a drink of water or juice will be better than nothing.

I share an apple with my horse before a ride and I always take a big bottle of water for afterwards."

Lucy Mason, aged 14, enjoys horse riding to keep fit.

During training

Children will often forget to drink, so try to introduce drinking as an integral part of training. Ensure children arrive with a drink and that they take it with them to the side of the pitch, court, pool or track and remind them to sip little and often.

Long training sessions and tournaments

Young athletes will need to top up their energy stores during longer training sessions of over an hour or during tournaments. Refuelling with carbohydrate on a regular basis will prevent the onset of fatigue. Whether this is solids or fluids will depend on the type of exercise and the individual child's preference. For older children, a target of 30 to 60g carbohydrate per hour will ensure blood sugar levels are sustained. This should be a medium- to high-GI snack which will be rapidly digested and converted into energy; a ripe banana, jam, marmite or peanut butter sandwich or bagel, malt loaf, flapjack, dried fruit or nuts, washed down with water or a diluted sports drink.

For full-day tournaments, you will usually need to provide your child with a nourishing packed lunch, plus snacks, to sustain their energy throughout the day. If there are 1–2 hours between events, children should have fluids and a light snack, perhaps a cereal bar, fruit bar, fresh fruit, a wholemeal bread sandwich (cheese, peanut butter, tuna), or mixed nuts and raisins. If there are more than 2 hours between events, then sandwiches, muffins, pasta salad, cereal and milk, creamy rice and fruit, yoghurt or pancakes will give good sustenance. If the break is longer than 3 hours then use this time to consume a larger meal. It's worth investing in a small flask so that your child can warm up with a hot drink or a nourishing soup during cold mid-winter tournaments.

After training

The magic window

For children training on a regular basis, quick recovery is vital. Young athletes need to recover efficiently in order to rehydrate, replenish muscle glycogen stores, repair muscle trauma and regenerate new muscle. Athletes who fail to do this risk suffering the effects of glycogen depletion over time. As glycogen stores are reduced, muscles become fatigued, energy levels fall and this, unfortunately, is often when injuries occur. The magic window for recovery is the first 30 minutes after exercise. The body is more efficient at converting nutrients during this time, so consuming a combination of carbohydrate and protein will promote rapid and efficient recovery; carbohydrate to replenish glycogen and protein to repair and restore the muscles. Encourage your child to take a post-training snack with them to their training session if they are not coming home immediately.

Milk, chocolate milk or drinking yoghurt make excellent post-exercise recovery drinks as they contain both a good carb to protein combo and plenty of electrolytes. If you can, combine this with a solid snack, such as eggs on toast, a cheese sandwich or a banana and yoghurt.

" I like to take a banana to an event and my favourite post-training snack is garlic bread and a milk shake."

Hugh Sadler, aged 13, trains 7 times a week, runs for Bristol & West AC, Avon county and south-west region. Also plays football (Independent Schools South-West trials), rugby, squash and tennis.

Ambition: "To run for England."

Post-training recovery meal

Follow the snack with a post-training meal within about 2 hours of training, when the timing allows. This meal should be balanced with plenty of carbohydrates, some protein, and a little fat and should include vegetables or fruit. Good options are a jacket potato with grilled fish and salad, a risotto with fish and vegetables, pasta with tomato sauce, lasagne and salad or chicken curry with rice.

If your child has late training, after the evening meal, ensure he or she consumes something straight after the session before bedtime; cereal with milk or a hot chocolate.

If your child is particularly tired despite adequate pre- and post-training fuelling, let the coach know. It may be that they are overdoing it and in need of a couple of days' rest.

Eating for the event

Consuming the right foods at the right time will ensure healthy and consistent training and give young athletes a nutritional and mental head-start for their best performance in competition, whether this is a race, match or tournament. Follow these tips for eating in the days leading up to an event and your child should arrive on the day well-fuelled, well-hydrated and feeling comfortable, with a healthy balance of pre-event nerves and confidence!

Top Tips **For pre-event fuelling**

1. During the four days leading up to an event, ensure your child's diet is particularly copious and healthy.

2. Meals should be balanced and nutrient-dense, including plenty of low- to medium-GI carbohydrates, lean protein and a small amount of fat.

3. Ensure your child drinks plenty of fluid; a combination of water, milk, fruit juice or squash, smoothies and high water-content foods (fruit, salad, veg, soups etc).

4. Snacks should be nutrient-dense. Offer snacks such as flapjacks, malt loaf and fruit rather than 'empty-calorie' foods such as crisps, biscuits, sweets or chips. Remember to use the Ferrari scenario (see page 12) to explain the reason why children need to fuel themselves with the good stuff!

5. Your child may have pre-event nerves, so avoid spicy, high-fibre or unfamiliar foods which may cause stomach upset. Stick to foods your child has eaten during training.

6. Higher-fat foods such as pasties, pies, cream and fried foods may make your child feel heavy and sluggish.

7. If children need to travel a long distance, or abroad, for a competition, make sure they are well supplied with water and snacks so they don't have to rely on expensive and invariably less-nutritious choices en route.

I love a big bowl of tagliatelle pasta with smoked salmon and crème fraîche the night before a 90-minute football match."

James Mason, aged 18, footballer, left back, FC Hausen am Albis, Switzerland.

"Too nervous and pent up to eat properly before a rugby match, my son has now developed his own pre-match ritual: a high energy meal the night before and then, in the morning, a small portion of cereal, plenty of milk and banana blinis (see page 74)."

© John Russell

Top Tips   For competition day

On competition day children need to eat just enough to top up muscle glycogen and keep blood glucose levels steady without overeating, as this can make them feel sluggish.

1. As with training, children should drink plenty of fluid and eat a meal 2–4 hours before the event. They may also need to top up energy stores with an easily digestible snack 1–2 hours before the event.

2. Encourage children who suffer from pre-event nerves to work out their own ritual for competition day, so that they feel comfortable with what to eat and when.

3. Don't try new foods on competition day as they might cause stomach upset; if a child doesn't usually eat porridge for breakfast before a swimming competition, this is not the day to try it for the first time!

4. Good hydration is key; use the urine chart (see page 39) to check hydration levels.

5. Avoid too many sugary snacks which will interfere with blood sugar levels. Bananas are a fantastic option. I class them as 'magic' because they help calm nerves, are easily digested, easy to transport and packed with potassium, vitamin C and vitamin B6.

6. For tournaments involving multiple games, long gaps between heats and finals of varying lengths, ensure your child has the wherewithal to refuel and rehydrate after each game or heat. Plan well, so that the child has enough sustenance to power through to a final!

7. Invest in a mini cold bag; sweaty sandwiches are never particularly appetising! Likewise, in the winter, a small Thermos is useful for warm drinks.

© Sean Biggs | Dreamstime.com

Pre-event breakfasts for Go Faster Kids

Porridge with honey and raisins

Wheat cereal or muesli with milk and chopped banana

Scrambled or poached eggs on toast

Oat pancakes with bananas, honey, maple or agave syrup

(see breakfast recipes on pages 64–83 for more examples)

If children are still hungry after this, then top up with wholemeal toast or English muffins with marmite, peanut butter, honey or jam

Pre- and mid-event snacks for Go Faster Kids

Handful of nuts and raisins

Slice of malt loaf

Banana

Energy bar or flapjack

Small sandwich (tuna, cheese, salad, chicken, peanut butter)

Light pasta salad (tuna or chicken with cucumber, sweetcorn or pesto)

Dried mango slices, dried apricots

Rice cakes, pitta bread, carrot or celery sticks with hummus

Water or sports drink (if appropriate), hot chocolate for a cold day

Rehydrate, Refuel, Rest

Children need to recover well after an event, particularly if they are going straight back into training.

Rehydrate

Young athletes should drink 250–500ml fluid within 15–30 minutes of finishing a competition or tournament game. When they get home, use the urine chart (see page 39) to check hydration levels. Drinks should be water or, if the child is dehydrated or has sweated a lot over a long period, then milk or a sports drink will replenish electrolytes lost through sweat.

Refuel

A carbohydrate/protein snack within the 30 minute 'magic recovery window', followed by a recovery meal within two hours will restore muscle glycogen, repair muscle tissue and help regenerate new muscle. High-GI carbohydrate food will be more rapidly digested and therefore kick-start the recovery process more effectively. Salty foods will help replace electrolytes. Children will be pleased to know that this is the time when treats such as pizza, steak or chicken and chips are actually good options!

© Studio1231 | Dreamstime.com

"I don't like eating straight after hard training and matches because I'm out of breath and it makes me feel a bit sick. When I've got my breath back, my favourite meal is chicken burger and chips."

Izzi Norman, aged 15, trains 7 times a week, county basketball player. Also likes to play netball, hockey, rounders, athletics and canoe polo "to keep fit and have fun!"

Rest

Adequate rest after competition is critically important if young athletes want to make progress in training and competition. It is when the body is resting that muscles heal, regain strength, adapt and grow. Children need to be encouraged to rest after both intense training and competition, especially those who find it hard to read their own bodies or who are training for multiple sports simultaneously. Children (and parents!) must watch out that their ambition does not win over common sense.

Post-exercise drink

Packed with carbohydrate, protein, calcium and potassium to kick-start
the recovery process, milk, or chocolate milk, makes an excellent
post-exercise drink.

Robert Poth, aged 15

GB Number 1 ski racer in year of birth, 2013
Winner of Czech Republic 2013 International Slalom Ski Race

Great Britain U16 Children's Ski Race Team, Hemel Ski Race Club

How often do you train?

Two hours a week after school at Hemel Ski Race Club and 4 hours a week Strength and Conditioning sessions later in the evening.

How often do you compete?

December to April, I have various National and International Alpine ski racing competitions throughout Europe during the Winter Race Season. April to October, I have dryland training and indoor ski racing in the UK.

Do you have a long-term ambition?

My main goal is to reach World Cup and Olympic standard. I want to compete at the highest standard possible for my sport, do my best for myself and my country.

How much do you know about eating for better performance?

I am a member of the Hertfordshire Talented Athlete Programme. They support me with Strength and Conditioning, Sport Psychology and Nutrition.

What about your diet?

My mum is a good cook and very interested in giving me and my brother the right nutrition. We always eat meals as a family at the dining room table.

What's your best breakfast?

Pain au chocolat, fruit, milk, yoghurt and guava juice.

Favourite meal for the night before a race?

I love to eat any pasta meal.

Do you take food with you to tournaments?

Always Go Faster Food date, apricot and walnut flapjacks!

Do you drink commercial energy drinks?

No, I don't believe in them! I take water or juice.

Go Faster recipes for kids

The following recipes will provide you with plenty of ideas for tasty, imaginative meals and snacks to fuel an active child's busy life. I have tried my best to marry the less-sophisticated tastes of the younger child with the, perhaps, more-sophisticated tastes of older adolescents and adults, so that you should get away with serving many of these recipes to the whole family. Likewise, older children who like to be let loose in the kitchen will be able to prepare most of these recipes themselves.

Each recipe is accompanied by a nutritional breakdown per portion. Portion sizes are fairly generous and, as appetites vary enormously from child to child and family to family, you may find that you need to adapt these accordingly. Each recipe is marked with an icon to indicate its suitability:

🏃 Healthy, sustaining, good for back-to-back training

⚡ Pre-exercise energy-boosting snack

🧘 Recovery post-exercise

Ⓥ Vegetarian

💷 Economy eats

You will also find an approximate guide to how long each recipe takes to prepare and cook so that you can plan around the family schedule.

Notes

• Oven temperatures are for gas or a standard fan oven.

• Eggs are large, free-range.

• Many of the recipes can also be easily adapted to suit vegetarians.

• Economy eat meals are estimated at under £2 per portion.

Part Two

Breakfast & Brunch

Go Faster Porridge, with Bananas, Toasted Walnuts and Maple Syrup

Prep 1 min Cook 8 mins

Whether fuelling up for a football match or just a normal school day, a bowl of porridge is guaranteed to sustain a child's energy levels.

Of course, porridge is just as good for adults; I rarely take on a long run without stocking up on porridge! Unlike sugary processed cereals, the carbohydrate in oats is released into the bloodstream slowly to prevent those 11 o'clock food cravings.

Ingredients to serve 2

60g jumbo porridge oats

450ml water or milk, or half water and half milk

pinch of salt

1 large banana, peeled and sliced thinly

handful of walnuts (optional)

1 heaped tsp maple syrup

Method

Preheat the oven to 160°C/gas mark 3, if using the walnuts.

Put the oats, water and/or milk into a pan with a pinch of salt. Bring to the boil over a high heat and then turn the heat down and simmer gently for about 5 minutes, stirring frequently. The porridge will become thick and creamy.

Meanwhile, pop the nuts onto a baking tray and roast in the oven for 5 minutes.

Pour the porridge into two warmed bowls, sprinkle with the bananas and nuts and drizzle over the maple syrup.

Throw in a handful of sultanas at the start of cooking or use blueberries instead of the banana. Replace the maple syrup with honey or agave syrup.

Nutrition per serving

Energy	Protein	Carbs	Sugars
359kcal	**11g**	**52g**	**25g**
Salt	Fibre	Fat	Saturates
0.5g	**5g**	**14g**	**3g**

Apple and Raisin Cinnamon Porridge

Prep 5 mins Cook 5 mins

Filling, satisfying, nourishing and packed with slow-release carbohydrate.

The addition of the low-GI apples and raisins helps sustain the release of energy from this porridge for even longer. Try out variations of this, using pears, for instance, or dried apricots. If you can get away with it, use the less refined, whole rolled porridge oats. They're more nutritious than the more refined or quick-cook varieties.

Ingredients to serve 2

60g jumbo porridge oats

225ml milk

225ml water

1 tbsp sugar

2 large apples, peeled, cored and diced

handful of raisins

½ tsp cinnamon

pinch of salt

honey, syrup or sugar to serve

Method

Put the oats, milk, water, sugar, apples, raisins and cinnamon into a pan.

Bring to the boil over a high heat and then turn the heat down and simmer the porridge gently, stirring frequently, for about 5 minutes, until thick and creamy.

Add the salt halfway through cooking.

Pour the porridge into warmed bowls and drizzle with honey or syrup, or sprinkle with a little sugar.

Do you hate to wash up after porridge? Just pour cold water into the pan immediately after serving and it cleans like magic! Jumbo oats don't stick nearly as badly as the refined ones.

Nutrition per serving

Energy	Protein		Carbs	Sugars
383kcal	**8g**		**83g**	**53g**
Salt	Fibre		Fat	Saturates
0.5g	**10g**		**5g**	**2g**

Crunchy Granola

Prep 2 mins Cook 20 mins

Kids love this tasty granola, brimming with nutritious energy, slow-burning carbohydrates, protein, healthy fats, vitamins and minerals.

Simple and speedy to make and so much tastier than shop-bought versions, this granola works just as well at breakfast time, with fresh fruit and yoghurt, as it does as a nutritious and tasty snack, straight from the jar.

Ingredients to serve 6

200g jumbo porridge oats

250g mixed nuts and seeds (flaked almonds, sunflower and pumpkin seeds, walnuts, pistachios, pecans and hazelnuts)

½ tsp cinnamon

½ tsp ground ginger

2 tbsp honey or maple syrup

2 tbsp sunflower oil

2 tbsp water

100g mixed dried fruit (raisins, crystallised ginger, dried apricots, figs and/or dates), chopped (optional)

Method

Preheat the oven to 180°C/gas mark 4.

Mix together the oats, nuts and seeds with the spices, honey or maple syrup, oil and water.

Spread the mixture evenly onto a large baking sheet.

Bake for 20 minutes until golden brown, turning the mixture after 10 minutes for it to brown evenly.

Leave to cool for 5 minutes or so. It will crisp up like magic.

Add the dried fruit, if using.

Store in an airtight container for up to three weeks.

Leave in a glass jar on the kitchen table for kids to snack on in favour of sugary, fat-laden shop-bought biscuits.

Nutrition per serving

Energy	Protein	Carbs	Sugars
455kcal	8g	83g	53g
Salt	Fibre	Fat	Saturates
0.5g	10g	5g	2g

Chocolate Peanut Granola

Prep 2 mins Cook 20 mins

It's more than wishful thinking; chocolate can be good for you!

Sweet, crunchy and delicious, this granola offers a healthier alternative to commercial chocolate breakfast cereals. Packed with a good balance of sustaining and unrefined carbohydrate, fibre, omega-3 fatty acids, protein and essential minerals, it even makes the milk turn chocolate-brown! Serve with milk or yoghurt and fresh fruit.

Ingredients to serve 6

200g jumbo porridge oats

100g roughly chopped skinless peanuts

2 tbsp cocoa powder

2 tbsp runny honey

2 tbsp water

2 tbsp sunflower or rapeseed oil

1 tsp cinnamon

1 dessert spoon soft brown sugar

½ tsp salt

chocolate chips, freeze-dried raspberries or strawberries, raisins or crystallised ginger (optional)

Method

Preheat the oven to 180°C/gas mark 4.

In a large bowl mix the porridge oats with the peanuts, cocoa powder, runny honey, water, oil, cinnamon, sugar and salt.

Spread the mixture onto a large baking sheet and bake in the oven for 15–20 minutes, turning every five minutes or so to prevent burning.

Leave to cool for 10 minutes; it will crisp up like magic!

If you like, you could add chocolate chips, freeze-dried raspberries or strawberries, raisins or crystallised ginger at this stage.

Store in an airtight container for up to three weeks.

Rich in antioxidants and important minerals such as copper, iron, potassium and magnesium, dark chocolate and cocoa can help boost the immune system.

Nutrition per serving

Energy	Protein	Carbs	Sugars
287kcal	**8g**	**34g**	**9g**

Salt	Fibre	Fat	Saturates
0.5g	**4g**	**16g**	**2g**

Maple and Almond Crisp

Prep 2 mins Cook 20 mins

A nutrient-dense breakfast or an after-school snack; particularly delicious with Greek yoghurt.

This recipe is packed with slow-burning carbohydrates and is rich in heart-healthy monounsaturated fat, vitamin E, bone-strengthening calcium and magnesium, as well as a host of other nutrients, including zinc and fibre. We like to create crispy clusters of granola by scrunching up the mixture on the baking tray before putting it in the oven.

Ingredients to serve 6

200g jumbo porridge oats

100g flaked almonds

½ tsp ground ginger

3 tbsp maple syrup

½–1 tbsp dark muscovado sugar

2 tbsp sunflower oil

2 tbsp water

Method

Preheat the oven to 180°C/gas mark 4.

Mix together the oats and nuts with the ginger, maple syrup, muscovado sugar, oil and water.

Spread the mixture evenly onto a large baking sheet. Scrunch the mixture into little clusters.

Bake for 20 minutes until golden brown, turning the mixture after 10 minutes for it to brown evenly.

Leave to cool for 5 minutes or so. It will crisp up like magic.

Store in an airtight container for up to three weeks.

Let kids munch on a bowl of maple and almond crisp while they do their homework.

Nutrition per serving

Energy	Protein	Carbs	Sugars
282kcal	**7g**	**35g**	**8g**
Salt	Fibre	Fat	Saturates
0.5g	**4g**	**13g**	**1g**

Rainbow Breakfast Crunch

Prep 2 mins No cook

Colourful, delicious and nutritious.

Perfectly balanced with carbohydrate, protein and fat, and brimming with a rainbow selection of superfood phytonutrients, the luscious red and white layers of this attractive dish will sustain kids through a hot summer's training morning.

Ingredients to serve 2 (generously)

200g soft fruit; either frozen, or whatever is in season – blackberries, blackcurrants, blueberries, raspberries, redcurrants, or strawberries

2 tsp sugar (optional)

500g natural yoghurt

4 tbsp maple and almond crisp (see page 69)

Method

Put the fruit in a bowl and, if using, sprinkle over the sugar.

In a tall glass or sundae dish, carefully arrange the yoghurt, maple and almond crisp and fruit in layers, to create colourful stripes, starting with the fruit and finishing with a good sprinkling of crunchy maple and almond crisp on top.

A great energy-packed breakfast or a mid-afternoon snack.

Nutrition per serving

Energy	Protein	Carbs	Sugars
493kcal	17g	62g	31g

Salt	Fibre	Fat	Saturates
0.3g	7g	20g	6g

American Blueberry Pancakes

Prep 5 mins Cook 5 mins

These mouth-wateringly light and fluffy pancakes will rapidly replenish muscle glycogen.

They'll also provide protein for muscle growth and repair. Prepare the mixture in advance, so you or your kids can cook the pancakes on arriving home to kick-start the recovery process as soon as possible. If using frozen blueberries, use straight from the freezer without defrosting.

Ingredients to serve 4

1 whole large, free-range egg, plus 1 egg white

200g self-raising flour, sifted

2 tsp baking powder

¼ tsp freshly grated nutmeg

¼ tsp ground cinnamon

pinch of salt

300ml buttermilk, or 150ml semi-skimmed milk mixed with 150ml natural yoghurt

2 tbsp melted butter or vegetable oil, plus a little more melted butter for frying

150g blueberries, fresh or frozen

extra blueberries and maple syrup or Demerara sugar to serve

Method

Whisk the egg white until it starts to form soft peaks.

In another bowl, combine the flour, baking powder, nutmeg, cinnamon and salt. Make a hole in the centre of this, break the egg into it and then add the buttermilk.

Stir the wet ingredients quickly into the dry using a wooden spoon. Don't worry too much if it's not very smooth. Add the melted butter or oil and the blueberries. Fold in the egg white.

Heat a pancake pan or non-stick frying pan and brush with a little melted butter. Cook 3–4 pancakes at a time over a gentle heat, using a heaped tablespoon of batter for each cake. Gently cook for a few minutes until bubbles start to appear on top, then flip over and cook for a couple of minutes on the other side until well risen and cooked through.

Serve immediately with extra blueberries and maple syrup, or just sprinkled with crunchy Demerara sugar.

Nutrition per serving

Energy	Protein	Carbs	Sugars
303kcal	11g	47g	8g

Salt	Fibre	Fat	Saturates
2g	3g	9g	2g

Banana Buttermilk Blinis

Prep 5 mins Cook 5 mins

These tasty, nutritious banana blinis are as light as a feather.

Bananas, packed with potassium, vitamin C and vitamin B6, transform these blinis into an effective and sustaining breakfast, pre-exercise energy-booster or teatime snack. If you have any left over, pop them in the lunchbox; they taste great cold.

Ingredients for 6–8 blinis

80g (3 tbsp) plain white flour

80g (3 tbsp) self-raising wholemeal flour

1 tsp baking powder

pinch of salt

handful of raisins (optional)

1 tsp caster sugar

250ml buttermilk (or natural yoghurt)

1 large or 2 small ripe bananas, mashed with a fork

1 large, free-range egg

1 tbsp sunflower oil

1 tbsp melted butter or sunflower oil to cook

sugar or syrup to serve (optional)

Method

In a mixing bowl, combine the flours, baking powder, salt, raisins and sugar.

In another bowl, briefly beat together the buttermilk, banana, egg and oil until combined and then pour into the flour mixture. Mix until just combined.

Leave the batter to stand for 5 minutes or, if you like, chill in the fridge for up to 24 hours.

Heat a pancake pan or non-stick frying pan to a medium heat and add a little oil or melted butter. Spoon tablespoons of the batter into the pan to form individual blinis of 8–10cm in diameter.

When little bubbles appear on the surface, flip the blinis and cook on the other side for another couple of minutes until well risen and cooked through.

Serve plain or with a little sugar or syrup.

Nutrition per serving

Energy	Protein	Carbs	Sugars
164kcal	5g	26g	7g

Salt	Fibre	Fat	Saturates
0.2g	2g	5g	2g

Food that is good for endurance is often good 'brain' food, these pancakes are my son's favourite pre-exam fuel-up snack!

Post-training Buckwheat Pancakes with Ham and Cheese

Prep 5 mins Cook 5 mins

Savoury pancakes are always a winner when the children bring home friends for lunch or supper.

A member of the rhubarb family, buckwheat in fact contains no wheat at all! Gluten-free and packed with minerals and fibre, it has a deliciously sweet, nutty flavour. Prepare the mixture in advance and quickly toss these pancakes together for a delicious post-training 'recovery' brunch to replenish energy stores and replace salts lost through sweat.

Ingredients for 8 pancakes

For the pancakes

100g buckwheat flour

50g plain flour, wholemeal or white (the addition of wheat flour improves the texture, but if you want to go gluten-free, use 150g buckwheat flour and omit the plain flour)

pinch of salt

1 large, free-range egg

100ml semi-skimmed milk

200ml water

30g melted butter, plus extra to cook

For the filling

8 thin slices of good-quality cooked ham

200g grated cheese – Emmental, Gruyère or Cheddar

Method

In a mixing bowl, combine the two flours and salt. Break the egg into the mixture and then add the milk and 100ml water. Whisk until the mixture is nice and smooth. Mix in the remaining water and the melted butter until the batter has the consistency of thin cream. If possible, leave
to rest for a few hours or overnight.

Heat a pancake pan or large non-stick frying pan over a medium heat and brush with a little melted butter. Lift the pan off the heat, add a small ladleful of the batter and quickly swirl it around to cover the bottom of the pan with a thin layer.

Cook the pancake for 2 minutes over a medium heat, or until it comes away easily from the pan when you shake it. Then toss the pancake over and cook for a minute or two on the other side.

Flip the pancake back over. Arrange a thin slice of ham and a tablespoon of grated cheese onto one half. Fold the plain half of the pancake over the filling and then fold in half again. Cook on a very gentle heat for a minute or two until the cheese has melted and serve immediately.

Nutrition per pancake

Energy	Protein	Carbs	Sugars
259kcal	12g	14g	1g

Salt	Fibre	Fat	Saturates
1.3g	1g	17.5g	10.5g

Oaty Hotcakes with Strawberries and Agave Nectar

Prep 5 mins Cook 5 mins

Serve as a tasty and sustaining brunch or breakfast.

Ultra-light and very delicious, these oaty hotcakes are well-balanced, packed with protein, slow-burning carbohydrate, vitamins, calcium and a host of minerals. Low in GI, agave nectar avoids the 'sugar rush' kids experience when they eat honey or golden syrup. A fantastic start to the day for active kids!

Ingredients for 8 hotcakes

400g strawberries, washed, drained and sliced quite thinly

4 tbsp agave nectar

150g wholemeal self-raising flour

50g jumbo porridge oats

½ tsp baking powder

½ tsp bicarbonate of soda

pinch of salt

15g caster sugar

2 large, free-range eggs, lightly beaten

150ml milk

40ml warm water

25g melted butter

knob of butter for frying

Method

Combine the strawberries and the agave nectar in a small saucepan and warm over a very gentle heat. Set aside.

Mix together the dry ingredients in a bowl and make a well for the eggs. Break the eggs into the well and then mix together quickly with a metal spoon, gradually adding the milk until you have a smooth batter.

Add the warm water and the melted butter. Don't let the mixture rest, use it immediately.

Heat a pancake pan or non-stick frying pan and melt a knob of butter in it. Cook 3–4 oatcakes at a time over a gentle heat, using a scant tablespoon of batter for each cake. Gently cook for a minute or two until bubbles start to appear on top, then flip over and cook for 1 minute on the other side.

Serve immediately with the strawberries and nectar spooned over the top.

Nutrition per serving

Energy	Protein	Carbs	Sugars
187kcal	6g	30g	14g

Salt	Fibre	Fat	Saturates
0.6g	3g	6g	3g

A natural sweetener from Mexico, agave nectar is extracted from the sap of the same plant that tequila is made from!

Apple Power Pancakes with Spiced Apple Syrup

Prep 5 mins Cook 5 mins

Supercharge your child's energy levels with these tasty little pancakes, packed with vitamins, fibre and slow-release carbohydrate.

Even my daughter who's not particularly keen on apples will tuck into these pancakes quite happily! Left to their own devices, older children should be perfectly capable of cooking these themselves; if you are feeling generous, you could prepare the mixture in advance for them!

Ingredients for 15 small pancakes

For the pancakes

400ml semi-skimmed milk

2 large, free-range eggs

1 tbsp sunflower oil or melted butter

1 tbsp caster sugar

120g porridge oats

200g plain flour

2 tsp baking powder

½ tsp ground ginger

pinch salt

1 large apple, peeled, cored and diced

For the syrup

40g butter

½ tsp cinnamon or mixed spice

1–2 tbsp Demerara sugar

2 large apples, peeled, cored and diced

Method

Put the milk, eggs, oil or melted butter, and sugar into a bowl and mix together.

Add the oats, flour, baking powder, ginger, salt and apple and mix until you have a thick, smooth batter.

Make the syrup – melt the butter, spice and Demerara sugar together in a small saucepan and then add the two remaining diced apples. Sauté gently for a couple of minutes until the apples are soft but still have their shape.

Heat a pancake pan or non-stick frying pan and melt a knob of butter in it. Cook 3–4 pancakes at a time over a gentle heat, using a tablespoon of batter for one. Gently cook for a minute or two until bubbles start to appear on top, then flip over and cook on the other side for a minute or two.

Serve the pancakes (about 3 per person) with the spiced apple syrup poured over the top and perhaps a little Demerara sugar sprinkled over for an extra crunch to power your children through the day!

Nutrition per pancake

Energy	Protein	Carbs	Sugars
159kcal	4g	25g	7g
Salt	Fibre	Fat	Saturates
0.6g	2g	5g	3g

Date and Walnut Breakfast Muffins with Cinnamon Streusel

Prep 5 mins Cook 15–20 mins

A fabulous energy breakfast or pre-training booster; weigh out the ingredients the night before to save time in the morning!

The secret to muffins is to avoid over-mixing; fold the wet ingredients quickly into the dry until they are just combined and then pop them into the oven. There's relatively little sugar in these muffins as the dates add enough sweetness. We usually eat them warm with butter and honey, which slightly defeats the object.

Ingredients for 12 muffins

For the muffins

150g white self-raising flour, sifted
150g wholemeal self-raising flour, sifted
pinch of salt
2 tsp baking powder
1 tsp bicarbonate of soda
80g soft brown sugar
½ tsp ginger
½ tsp cinnamon
75g chopped walnuts
120g dates, chopped
2 large, free-range eggs
90ml vegetable oil
1 tbsp runny honey
80ml semi-skimmed or skimmed milk
80ml low-fat natural yoghurt

For the cinnamon streusel topping

1 tbsp Demerara sugar
1 tbsp plain flour
½ tsp cinnamon
25g butter, softened

Method

Preheat the oven to 180°C/gas mark 4. Line a muffin tray with 12 muffin cases.

Make the cinnamon streusel topping: mix together the sugar, flour and cinnamon and then add the butter and rub in with your fingers until you have a crumbly mixture. Set aside.

Mix the white and wholemeal flour, salt, baking powder, bicarbonate of soda, sugar and spices together. Add the walnuts and dates and combine.

Break the eggs into a separate bowl and add the oil, honey, milk and yoghurt.

Beat very lightly with a fork then pour the mixture into the bowl with the dry ingredients and combine quickly. The mixture will appear lumpy, but don't worry, just spoon it into the muffin cases, sprinkle the cinnamon streusel on top and pop into the oven for 15–20 minutes. The muffins will rise and turn golden brown.

Eat while still warm or cool on a wire rack.

Nutrition per serving

Energy	Protein	Carbs	Sugars
286kcal	6g	35g	17g

Salt	Fibre	Fat	Saturates
0.4g	2g	14g	2.5g

Wholesome and nutritious, rich in slow-release carbohydrate, antioxidants, minerals and fibre, a great excuse to eat cake for breakfast!

Go Faster Breakfast Rock Cakes

Prep 5 mins Cook 20 mins

An excellent grab-and-go breakfast snack before early morning training or when pushed for time.

A more nutritious version of the traditional rock cake, these tasty little snacks are packed with low-GI carbohydrate, omega-3 essential fatty acids and antioxidants, ideal to boost children's energy levels at any time of day.

Ingredients for 24 rock cakes

60g walnuts, roughly chopped

1 large, free-range egg

60g butter, softened

30g soft brown sugar

60g runny honey

1 tbsp (30g) golden syrup

100g jumbo porridge oats

100g finely grated carrots

60g raisins

60g soft dried apricots, chopped

60g soft dried stoned dates, chopped

½ tsp ground nutmeg

½ tsp ground cinnamon

100g self-raising wholemeal flour

pinch of salt

½ tsp bicarbonate of soda

Method

Preheat the oven to 180°C/gas mark 4. Place the walnuts on a baking tray and toast in the oven for 5 minutes. Remove and leave to cool.

Lightly grease two baking trays with a little butter.

Place the egg, butter, sugar, honey and syrup in a large bowl and beat until smooth and creamy.

Stir in the oats, carrots, raisins, apricots, dates, walnuts and spices.

Add the flour, salt and bicarbonate of soda and stir to combine. The mixture will be a soft dough-like consistency.

Form little rocky mounds with a dessert spoon on the baking trays, leaving space between each mound for the mixture to spread a little.

Bake in the oven for 15 minutes, or until golden. With a spatula, transfer the cookies to a cooling tray and leave to cool and crisp up.

These keep for several days stored in an airtight container.

Nutrition per serving

Energy	Protein	Carbs	Sugars
99kcal	**2g**	**15g**	**7.5g**
Salt	Fibre	Fat	Saturates
0.1g	**1.5g**	**4g**	**1.5g**

Go Faster Full English

Prep 2 mins Cook 10 mins

Using quality ingredients, a full English breakfast can be a guilt-free pleasure!

What's so bad about a full English? Tomatoes and mushrooms, packed with healthy vitamins and anti-oxidants, eggs, a complete protein, containing the whole spectrum of amino acids, then baked beans and granary toast to add another punch of protein, plus fibre and plenty of slow-release carbs. Grill the bacon on a rack so unwanted fats will drip away.

Ingredients to serve 4

8 rashers of good-quality smoked or unsmoked back bacon, trimmed of excess fat

1 scant tbsp olive or rapeseed oil

200g button mushrooms

200g cherry tomatoes, on the vine if possible

1 large can of baked beans

4 slices granary or wholemeal bread

1 small knob of butter

8 large, free-range eggs, lightly beaten

pinch of salt and freshly ground pepper

Method

Preheat the grill or griddle to a high heat, lay the bacon rashers on the rack, and cook until crispy.

Add the oil to a non-stick frying pan and on a high heat, sauté the button mushrooms. When the mushrooms are almost cooked, turn down the heat and add the cherry tomatoes. Sauté gently until just starting to soften.

Meanwhile heat the beans in a small saucepan or in the microwave. Toast the bread, spread with butter and cut into triangles.

Season the eggs. On a medium heat, melt a small knob of butter in a non-stick saucepan. When the butter starts to sizzle, pour in the eggs. Turn the heat down to low and scramble the eggs, stirring slowly until the mixture begins to thicken and starts to become creamy. Remove from the heat while still slightly runny to prevent the eggs from overcooking.

Divide everything between four plates and serve with homemade ketchup (see page 164).

Nutrition per serving

Energy	Protein	Carbs	Sugars
558kcal	**36g**	**35g**	**8g**

Salt	Fibre	Fat	Saturates
1.6g	**8g**	**29g**	**9g**

Let the kids loose in the kitchen to cook their own full English – a useful skill to have for when they leave home!

Huevos Rancheros (Mexican Scrambled Eggs with Chorizo)

Prep 5 mins Cook 10 mins

A delicious concoction of Mexican flavours for a perfect Sunday brunch or nutritious 'fast-food' meal.

Most kids adore chorizo sausage and, used cleverly, it can be an excellent vehicle for tempting children into being more adventurous with foods such as the peppers, fresh herbs and chilli in this dish. You may want to serve the onion and chilli separately; those who love these can help themselves to more, and those who don't can easily avoid them!

Ingredients to serve 4

4 tortilla wraps

200g chorizo sausage, outer skin removed, sliced into fairly thin 3mm rounds

1 red pepper, seeds removed and sliced thinly

8 large, free-range eggs, lightly beaten

pinch of salt and freshly ground black pepper

1 spring onion, finely sliced

2 fresh green chillies, seeds removed and very finely sliced

1 tbsp fresh coriander, finely chopped

a few baby tomatoes (optional)

1 avocado, peeled and sliced (optional)

Method

Preheat the oven to 180°C/gas mark 4. Wrap the tortillas in tin foil and warm in the oven for a few minutes.

Gently sauté the chorizo slices in a non-stick frying pan for a couple of minutes on each side. (You won't need oil; the chorizo will crisp up in its own fat).

Add the red pepper and sauté for a further 2 minutes. Transfer the chorizo and red pepper to a warmed plate with a slotted spoon. Leave the excess oil in the pan to cook the eggs in.

Season the eggs with salt and a few grinds of black pepper. Return the pan to a gentle heat and pour in the egg mixture. Slowly stir until the eggs start to thicken and become creamy. Remove from the heat while still slightly runny to prevent overcooking.

Gently fold the chorizo, red pepper, spring onion, chillies and coriander into the eggs. Place a tortilla on each plate and pile the mixture on top. Garnish with baby tomatoes and avocado if you like.

Processed meat, including chorizo, is best eaten in moderation, as it can have high levels of salt and saturated fat.

Nutrition per serving

Energy	Protein	Carbs	Sugars
615kcal	33g	32g	2g
Salt	Fibre	Fat	Saturates
1.6g	4.2g	40g	10.5g

Mains

Prepare & Cook in under 20 Minutes

Spaghetti with Brown Shrimps, Peas and Pancetta

Prep 5 mins Cook 10 mins

Packed with low-GI carbohydrate, protein, good fats, vitamins and essential minerals to boost and maintain energy levels.

If you're looking for a delicious, healthy and sustaining meal, then you can't go wrong with this tasty spaghetti dish. Bursting with flavour, brown shrimps are generally found ready peeled and vacuum-packed at the fishmongers or at the fish counter in the supermarket. You could use small frozen prawns as an alternative.

Ingredients to serve 4

400g spaghetti

1 tbsp olive oil

100g cubed pancetta

1 clove garlic, finely sliced

250g frozen peas

200g pack of brown shrimps

1 red chilli, seeds removed
and finely sliced

½ tsp mild chilli powder or paprika

25g flat-leaf parsley, roughly chopped

2 tbsp crème fraîche

salt and freshly ground black pepper

Parmesan shavings to serve

Method

Bring a large pan of salted water to the boil and cook the spaghetti according to the instructions on the pack.

Meanwhile, heat 1 tbsp olive oil in a large frying pan and fry the pancetta for about 5 minutes, turning it around in the pan every now and then until it crisps up.

Add the garlic, gently sauté for a minute, then stir in the peas (pop them in the pan straight from the freezer; you don't need to defrost them first). Sauté on a low heat for another couple of minutes.

Stir in the shrimps, chilli, chilli powder, parsley and crème fraîche and cook gently for another couple of minutes. Season with a little salt and plenty of freshly ground black pepper, according to taste.

Drain the spaghetti, reserving just a small ladleful of the cooking water to prevent the pasta sticking. Add the pasta and the ladleful of cooking water to the sauce in the frying pan and stir to combine.

Serve in warmed pasta bowls with shavings of Parmesan and a few more grinds of black pepper.

Nutrition per serving

Energy	Protein	Carbs	Sugars
661kcal	**32.5g**	**81.5g**	**6g**

Salt	Fibre	Fat	Saturates
2.2g	**8g**	**23g**	**9.5g**

Lemony Pappardelle with King Prawns

Prep 3 mins Cook 10 mins

This pasta dish is simple, tasty, healthy and fast!

Light on the stomach yet sustaining and full of goodness, this pasta dish is packed with slow-burning carbohydrate, vitamin C, low-fat protein and plenty of minerals to help power young athletes through day-to-day training.

Ingredients to serve 4

400g pappardelle

zest of two lemons

3 tbsp extra virgin olive oil

1 or 2 garlic cloves, peeled and finely sliced

200–300g large raw prawns

1 small red chilli, sliced finely (optional)

2 tbsp lemon juice

100g bag of rocket or a large bunch of fresh flat-leaf parsley

freshly ground black pepper

shavings of Parmesan or pecorino (use a potato peeler to get thin shavings)

Method

Cook the pappardelle in plenty of salted boiling water according to pack instructions.

Meanwhile add the lemon zest to one tbsp of the olive oil and warm in a small saucepan for a few minutes over a low heat. Do not let the oil bubble. Take off the heat and leave to infuse.

In a large frying pan, add the remaining oil and gently sauté the garlic until just slightly golden. Remove from the pan with a slotted spoon. Add the prawns and sauté for 2–3 minutes until they are pink and just cooked through.

Drain the pappardelle when it is ready, reserving a tbsp of the cooking liquid and spoon it into the pan with the prawns. Add the reserved cooking liquid, the garlic, the lemony olive oil, the chilli, if using, the lemon juice and the rocket or parsley and toss everything together.

Serve in warmed pasta bowls with plenty of black pepper and Parmesan shavings (use a potato peeler to get thin shavings).

Nutrition per serving

Energy	Protein	Carbs	Sugars
549kcal	31.5g	75g	4g
Salt	Fibre	Fat	Saturates
2.9g	4.5g	14.5g	3.5g

Buy frozen prawns when they're on special offer for speedy meals like this one, they're packed with protein, good fats and minerals.

Fresh Tagliatelle with Creamy Walnut Sauce and Crispy Bacon Lardons

Prep 1 min Cook 10 mins

A quick and easy midweek staple, packed with hidden goodness.

Delicious, sustaining and nutritious, this low-GI meal takes minutes to prepare and is crammed with carbohydrate, protein, omega-3 essential fatty acids, antioxidants and minerals.

Ingredients to serve 4

400g fresh tagliatelle

100g walnuts

200g bacon lardons

100g creamy soft cheese

1 small garlic clove, crushed

squeeze of lemon juice

pinch of grated nutmeg

salt and plenty of freshly ground black pepper

a few leaves of basil or fresh flat-leaf parsley to serve

As well as being good for the heart and brain, walnuts can also help to reduce muscle inflammation.

Method

Preheat the oven to 180°C/gas mark 4.

Bring a large pan of salted water to the boil, and cook the tagliatelle according to the instructions on the pack.

Arrange the walnuts on a baking tray and bake in the oven for 5 minutes until lightly toasted. Remove from the oven, leave to cool, then blitz in a food processor until finely chopped.

Meanwhile, heat a small frying pan and sauté the lardons for five minutes, or until nicely crisp and golden. You won't need to add oil, the lardons will cook in their own fat. Remove from the pan with a slotted spoon and place on kitchen paper to soak up the excess fat.

In a small bowl, combine the walnuts with the soft cheese, garlic, lemon juice, nutmeg and seasoning.

Drain the pasta when it is cooked, reserving a small ladleful of the cooking water. Return the pasta and reserved water to the pan, stir in the cheese mixture and combine.

Serve the pasta in warmed bowls, scatter with the crispy lardons and decorate with some basil or parsley leaves.

Nutrition per serving

Energy	Protein	Carbs	Sugars
663kcal	27g	57g	1g

Salt	Fibre	Fat	Saturates
1.4g	4g	37g	11g

Lamb, Carrot and Pine Nut Meatballs

Prep 5 mins Chill 30 mins Cook 10 mins

These tasty meatballs are succulent little nutrition bombs.

Well-balanced with protein, vitamins A, C and K, vitamin B6, thiamin, niacin, potassium and omega-3s, these meatballs taste even better if you allow the flavours to infuse by refrigerating them for a few hours before cooking.

Ingredients to make 38–40 meatballs

1 small onion (about 50g), very finely chopped

1 garlic clove, crushed

1 small carrot (about 80g), finely grated

400g lamb mince

40g pine nuts, ground in a spice grinder or with a pestle and mortar (you could use 40g ground almonds as an alternative)

1 egg, lightly beaten

2 tsp ground coriander

1 tbsp finely chopped mint leaves

salt and freshly ground black pepper

1 tbsp olive oil

1 tbsp sunflower oil for frying the meatballs

Method

Gently fry the onion and the garlic in the olive oil until soft and translucent. Leave to cool for a couple of minutes.

Grind the pine nuts in a spice grinder or crush with a pestle and mortar.

Spoon the onion mixture into a large bowl and then add all the other ingredients except the sunflower oil. Mix with a wooden spoon or with your hands until everything is well combined.

Form small balls with your hands, about 1½–2cm in diameter, the size of a large marble. If you have time, cover and leave in the fridge for at least 30 minutes.

Heat the sunflower oil in a large frying pan and fry the meatballs for about 6 minutes, turning every two minutes so that they are golden-brown all over.

Serve in warmed pittas with some salad and homemade ketchup (see page 164).

Nutrition per serving

Energy	Protein	Carbs	Sugars
318kcal	24.5g	3.5g	2.5g
Salt	Fibre	Fat	Saturates
0.8g	1.5g	23g	6g

Instead of homemade ketchup, try serving with salsa or spicy yoghurt sauce.

Marinated Lemon Chicken Kebabs

Prep 10 mins Marinate 1–24 hours Cook 10 mins

Serve with plain couscous or quinoa for a balanced and sustaining meal.

Even the fussiest of kids adore these kebabs! Packed with flavoursome goodness including high-quality protein, vitamins and minerals, they taste delicious cooked on the barbecue or griddle and make an easy midweek supper or weekend lunch.

Ingredients to serve 4

4 metal or bamboo skewers

4 boneless, skinless free-range chicken breasts, cut into 3cm fairly large cubes

4 tbsp olive oil

2 lemons, juice and zest

2 garlic cloves, unpeeled, crushed with the flat side of a knife

2 tsp coriander seed, roughly ground with a pestle and mortar

1 tsp mild paprika

2 tsp oregano, tarragon or thyme

salt and freshly ground black pepper

Method

To marinade; place the chicken cubes into a mixing bowl and add the rest of the ingredients. Cover and chill for anything from 1 to 24 hours to let the flavours infuse.

If you are using bamboo skewers, soak them in a bowl of water for 30 minutes or so before using them so that they don't burn when you cook the kebabs.

Thread the chicken cubes onto the kebab sticks. Keep the marinade for basting.

Heat the griddle, grill or barbecue so that it is really hot and cook the kebabs for about 10 minutes, turning and basting with the marinade every few minutes, until crisp and brown on the outside and just cooked through on the inside. Take care not to overcook, as the chicken will go dry.

Serve with warmed pitta bread, rice or couscous and a little chilli sauce.

Nutrition per serving

Energy	Protein	Carbs	Sugars
252kcal	27g	2g	1.5g

Salt	Fibre	Fat	Saturates
0.3g	0.5g	15g	3g

Cook double the quantity, they taste great served cold as a lunchbox treat.

Lime Chilli Prawn Skewers with Chilli Mayo & Salsa

Prep 10 mins Marinate 10-15 mins Cook 4 mins

Perfect for a summer barbecue, these prawns are also a great source of protein.

Rich in B-vitamins, omega-3 fatty acids, iron, copper, magnesium and zinc, prawn kebabs will help muscle recovery and growth and give the immune system a boost. Get the kids to prepare and cook these themselves, they're quick, easy and delicious.

Ingredients to serve 4

4 metal or bamboo skewers

For the kebabs
16 raw tiger or king prawns, shelled

juice and zest of 2 limes

1 garlic clove, peeled and crushed

1 red chilli, deseeded and finely chopped

salt and freshly ground black pepper

2 tbsp olive oil

1 tbsp light soy sauce

For the chilli mayo
4 tbsp mayonnaise

1 tbsp sweet chilli sauce

For the salsa
See page 130

Method

If you are using bamboo skewers, soak them in a bowl of water for 30 minutes or so before using them so that they don't burn when you cook the prawns.

Place the prawns in a mixing bowl and add the rest of the ingredients. Set aside for 10 minutes to let the flavours infuse.

Meanwhile, mix together the mayonnaise with the sweet chilli sauce in a small bowl.

Thread the prawns onto the skewers. Keep the marinade for basting.

Heat the griddle, grill or barbecue so that it is really hot and cook the skewers for 3–4 minutes, turning and basting with the marinade, until the prawns are pink and just cooked through. Take care not to overcook, as the prawns will turn rubbery.

Serve with warmed pitta bread, plenty of salad and the chilli mayo and/or salsa.

Nutrition per serving

Energy	Protein	Carbs	Sugars
333kcal	8.5g	9.5g	8.5g
Salt	Fibre	Fat	Saturates
2.5g	1.5g	29g	4.5g

Keep packs of raw prawns in the freezer, they're a great source of protein, omega-3 fatty acids, copper, iron, magnesium and zinc.

Moorish Lamb Kebabs with Minty Yoghurt Sauce

Prep 10 mins   Marinate 1–24 hours   Cook 10 mins

Moorish and moreish; a mouth-watering taste of the sun.

Packed with good quality protein, these kebabs are really good with a dollop of garlicky yoghurt sauce or homemade tomato ketchup. Serve with saffron rice or couscous for a balanced meal with plenty of low-GI carbohydrate to maintain energy levels.

Ingredients to serve 4

8 metal or bamboo skewers

For the kebabs

600g lamb fillet or boneless lamb leg, trimmed and cut into 2.5cm cubes

selection of vegetables cut into 2.5cm pieces, for instance a courgette, a red or yellow pepper, deseeded, and/or button mushrooms

For the marinade

3 tbsp olive oil

juice and zest of 1 lemon

2 garlic cloves

1 tsp cumin seeds, roughly ground with a pestle and mortar

2 tbsp coriander seeds, roughly ground with a pestle and mortar

1 tsp sweet smoked paprika (optional)

salt and freshly ground black pepper

Yoghurt sauce

200g low-fat natural yoghurt

1 garlic clove

25g bunch fresh mint leaves, finely chopped

salt and freshly ground black pepper

Method

Place the cubes of lamb into a mixing bowl and add the marinade ingredients. Leave for up to 24 hours to let the flavours infuse.

If you are using bamboo skewers, soak them in a bowl of water for about 30 minutes before using them so that they don't burn when you cook the kebabs.

While the skewers are soaking, combine all the ingredients of the yoghurt sauce in a small bowl.

Thread the meat and vegetables onto the kebab sticks. Keep the marinade for basting.

Heat the griddle, grill or barbecue so that it is really hot and cook the kebabs for about 10 minutes, turning and basting with the marinade every few minutes, until crisp and brown on the outside and slightly pink on the inside.

Serve with the yoghurt sauce and saffron rice (see page 93).

Nutrition per serving

Energy	Protein	Carbs	Sugars
350kcal	**36g**	**6g**	**3g**

Salt	Fibre	Fat	Saturates
1g	**0.5g**	**23g**	**8g**

Saffron Rice

Prep 5 mins Cook 15 mins

Temptingly aromatic, saffron rice is simple and quick to make, and is a perfect accompaniment to kebabs, salmon steaks, tagines and casseroles.

A relatively slow-burning carbohydrate, basmati rice is nutritious, easy to digest and an excellent fuel for any young athlete wanting to eat for endurance. Saffron adds colour and flavour, but it is expensive and can be easily omitted.

Ingredients to serve 4

100g unsalted butter

1 cinnamon stick

6 cardamom pods, bruised with a pestle and mortar

1 bay leaf

4 crushed black peppercorns

250g white basmati rice, rinsed until the water runs clear and drained

50g flaked almonds
(pistachios are also nice as an alternative)

75g dried cranberries (find them with the sultanas and raisins in the supermarket)

pinch of saffron, soaked in a few tbsp boiling water and left to infuse for 10 minutes

salt

freshly chopped parsley or coriander (optional)

Method

Pour the rice into a sieve and rinse under cold running water until the water runs clear.

Soak the saffron threads in a tablespoon of boiling water and leave to infuse for 10 minutes.

Melt the butter in a large saucepan and then add the cinnamon stick, cardamom, bay leaf and black peppercorns. Gently sauté over a low heat for a few minutes until you start to smell the aroma of the spices.

Add the rice and stir to coat with the butter and spices. Add the nuts, cranberries and saffron water, then pour over enough water to cover the rice by about 2cm. Add some salt at this stage.

Bring to the boil, cover tightly and simmer gently for 10 minutes, or until the rice is cooked.

The rice will soak up the water, so you will not have to drain it.

Fluff up with a fork and serve, sprinkled with the fresh parsley or coriander, if using.

Nutrition per serving

Energy	Protein	Carbs	Sugars
526kcal	8g	60g	7g
Salt	Fibre	Fat	Saturates
0.9g	1.5g	25g	13g

Almonds give omega-3s, vitamin E and a mineral punch of magnesium and potassium. Cranberries add antioxidants and heaps of vitamin C.

Go Faster Pad Thai Noodles

Prep 5 mins Cook 15 mins

A Go Faster speedy version of this popular dish; not exactly authentic, but healthy and adored by noodle-loving kids.

Substitute the chicken with prawns, bean curd, tofu, or stir fry vegetables if you like, and add more chilli if your children prefer a bit of a kick to their food.

Ingredients to serve 4

200g linguini-shaped rice noodles

1 tbsp sunflower oil

2 large, free-range eggs, lightly beaten

1 garlic clove, crushed

1 red chilli, seeds removed and finely chopped

1 tbsp lime juice

2 tbsp fish sauce

1 tbsp chilli sauce

1 tbsp brown sugar

2 boneless, skinless chicken breasts or thighs, sliced thinly

200g pack beansprouts

3 spring onions, finely sliced

3 tbsp unsalted peanuts, roughly chopped

25g bunch fresh coriander, roughly chopped

1 lime, cut into wedges

Method

Prepare the rice noodles according to the pack instructions. When they are ready, drain them and rinse them in cold water. Set aside.

Heat a drop of sunflower oil in a large wok or deep frying pan and add the eggs. As soon as they begin to set, gently stir them until they form a flattish omelette. Transfer to a plate, leave to set and cut into strips.

In a small bowl, combine the garlic, chilli, lime juice, fish sauce, chilli sauce and sugar.

Pour the rest of the sunflower oil into the wok and, over a medium heat, fry the chicken for a few minutes, until just cooked. Add the beansprouts and the spring onions, and stir-fry for another minute. Add the noodles and stir-fry for 2 minutes.

Add the peanuts, the coriander and the egg strips and then stir in the sauce.

Serve on large warmed plates with lime wedges.

Nutrition per serving

Energy	Protein		Carbs	Sugars
488kcal	29.5g		50.5g	13g
Salt	Fibre		Fat	Saturates
1.5g	4.5g		19g	4g

Keep packs of noodles in the store cupboard for a wholesome, quick-fix way to use up left-overs from the Sunday roast.

Go Faster
Steak Haché Burgers

Prep 2 mins Chill 30 mins Cook 8 mins

Just the best-quality pure beef smooshed together; delicious, healthy and always popular!

You'll have made these in no time at all and, made from scratch, you can rest assured that you know exactly what's in them. Whether you use a griddle, barbecue, or frying pan, it must be really hot before you cook these burgers to ensure a good, dark, sweet crust on the outside and a moist, juicy inside.

Ingredients to make 4 burgers

400g good-quality minced beef, not too lean, chuck steak is good

1 tsp dried thyme

½ tsp salt

plenty of freshly ground black pepper

potato rösti (see page 160), sauté potatoes or French bread to serve

Method

Place all the ingredients in a mixing bowl. Mix together with your hands until combined and then shape into four equal-sized patties. If you use a large cookie cutter or burger shaper you can make them look quite professional. Chill in the fridge for 30 minutes to allow to firm up.

Preheat the griddle, frying pan or barbecue to really hot and then cook the steaks for two minutes each side if you like them quite rare, or 4 minutes each side if prefer them well-done, turning just once.

Serve with potato rösti, sauté potatoes or in a piece of French bread with salad and ketchup.

Nutrition per serving

Energy	Protein	Carbs	Sugars
199kcal	**19g**	**0.5g**	**0g**
Salt	Fibre	Fat	Saturates
0.9g	**0g**	**13.5g**	**6g**

Juicy Beef Burger

Prep 5 mins Chill 30 mins Cook 10 mins

These substantial beef burgers are succulent and packed with protein.

It's hard to detect the very finely grated carrot mixed into these tasty burgers. This makes them ideal for children who struggle to eat their five a day. Prepare the burgers a few hours in advance and chill them for the best results.

Ingredients to make 4 burgers

½ tbsp olive oil

1 small onion, peeled and very finely chopped

400g good-quality minced beef, not too lean, chuck steak is good

1 medium carrot, very finely grated

1 garlic clove, peeled and very finely chopped or crushed

1 tsp dried thyme

plenty of salt and freshly ground black pepper

4 thin slices of cheddar cheese (optional)

To serve

4 ciabatta rolls

salad – little gem lettuce leaves, slices of tomato, cucumber slices

relish, mustard or homemade ketchup (see page 164)

gherkins, sliced

Method

Heat the olive oil in a small frying pan and very gently sauté the onion for about 3 minutes, until soft. Set aside to cool for a minute or two.

Place all the ingredients for the burger in a mixing bowl. Mix together with your hands until combined and then shape into four equal-sized patties. If you use a large cookie cutter or burger shaper you can make the burgers look quite professional. Chill in the fridge for 30 minutes to allow the burgers to firm up.

Preheat the griddle, frying pan or barbecue to really hot and then cook the burgers for two minutes each side if you like them quite rare, or 4 minutes each side if you prefer them well-done, turning just once. If using cheese, top each burger with a slice towards the end of the cooking time.

Cut the ciabatta rolls in half and toast, cut side down on the griddle, pan or barbecue.

Assemble the burgers, adding each person's preferred salad and/or relishes.

Nutrition per serving

Energy	Protein	Carbs	Sugars
449kcal	**29g**	**38g**	**8.5g**
Salt	Fibre	Fat	Saturates
2.9g	**3g**	**20.5g**	**8.5g**

Sweet Chilli Pork Burgers with Mango Salsa

Prep 5 mins Chill 30 mins Cook 8 mins

An excellent post-workout snack or healthy evening meal that kids will love!

Rich in carbohydrate to replenish depleted glycogen stores, with a moderate amount of protein to help muscle repair and the added benefit of ginger, which has excellent anti-inflammatory properties, these juicy burgers will help the body recover after hard exercise.

Ingredients to make 4 burgers

400g pork mince

1 tbsp sweet chilli sauce, plus extra to serve

1 tsp fresh ginger, finely grated

1 tbsp fresh coriander leaves, finely chopped

1 garlic clove, peeled and crushed

1 tbsp red pepper, finely chopped

1 tsp runny honey

plenty of salt and freshly ground black pepper

For the salsa

1 mango (not too ripe), peeled and diced

½ cucumber, diced

2 spring onions, finely sliced

2 tbsp fresh coriander leaves, finely chopped

1 tbsp fresh mint leaves, finely chopped

pinch of chilli powder

½ tsp ground coriander

½ tbsp extra virgin olive oil

juice of ½ a lime

To serve

4 ciabatta rolls or pittas

8 crisp gem lettuce leaves

Method

Place all the ingredients for the burger in a mixing bowl. Mix together with your hands until combined and then shape into four equal-sized patties. If you use a large cookie cutter or burger shaper you can make the burgers look quite professional. Chill in the fridge for at least 30 minutes to allow the burgers to firm up.

Meanwhile, combine all the ingredients for the salsa in a small bowl, cover and chill until required.

Preheat a griddle, frying pan or barbecue to hot and then cook the burgers for about 4 minutes each side until just cooked through, turning just once.

Cut the ciabatta rolls in half and toast, cut side down, on the griddle, pan or barbecue, or warm the pittas and slice an opening for the burger and salsa to slot into.

Assemble the burgers, adding a gem lettuce leaf, a spoon of salsa and/or sweet chilli sauce.

Nutrition per serving

Energy	Protein	Carbs	Sugars
442kcal	**4g**	**92g**	**9.4g**

Salt	Fibre	Fat	Saturates
0.5g	**3.4g**	**8g**	**1.5g**

Spicy Lamb Patties

Prep 5 mins Chill 30 mins Cook 6 mins

Children and adults alike, these mouth-watering lamb patties will put a smile on the face.

Delicious stuffed into warmed pitta bread and drizzled with spicy yoghurt sauce, these patties are surprisingly wholesome. Packed with protein and immune-boosting minerals, they are particularly good for fuelling a young athlete's busy training schedule.

Ingredients to make 8 burgers

400g lamb mince

1 small onion, peeled and finely chopped

1 garlic clove, peeled and crushed

1 tbsp olive oil

1 tsp fresh ginger, finely grated

1 tsp cumin seeds, crushed in a pestle and mortar

1 tsp coriander seeds, crushed in a pestle and mortar

1 tsp turmeric powder

½ tsp salt

freshly ground black pepper

1 tbsp fresh coriander leaves, finely chopped

1 tbsp fresh mint leaves, finely chopped

1 tsp fresh green chilli, very finely chopped

To serve

4 large pitta breads

spicy yoghurt sauce (see page 113)

salad leaves, tomatoes and cucumber

Method

Heat the olive oil in a small frying pan and very gently sauté the onion and garlic for about 3 minutes, until soft.

Place all the ingredients for the patties in a mixing bowl. Mix together with your hands until combined and then shape into eight equal-sized patties. Use a 5cm/2in cookie cutter to shape the patties. Chill in the fridge for 30 minutes to allow the patties to firm up.

Preheat a griddle, frying pan or barbecue to hot and then cook the patties for about 3 minutes on each side until just cooked through, turning just once.

Toast the pitta bread and cut in half so that you have 8 pockets for the lamb patties.

Assemble, adding one patty, a little spicy yoghurt sauce and some rocket leaves to each pitta pocket.

Nutrition per serving

Energy	Protein	Carbs	Sugars
353kcal	**13g**	**31g**	**4g**
Salt	Fibre	Fat	Saturates
1.1g	**2g**	**20g**	**9g**

Lentil and Sweet Potato Burgers

Prep 15 mins Chill 30 mins Cook 6 mins

Burgers don't have to be a carnivore heaven! These veggie burgers are packed with flavour and nutritious goodness.

Lentils and sweet potatoes not only provide high quality low-GI carbohydrate and protein to stabilise blood sugar levels and sustain energy for exercise and good concentration, they're also supercharged with vitamins, antioxidants and minerals to promote optimum health.

Ingredients to make 4 burgers

1 large sweet potato, peeled and diced

½ tbsp sunflower oil

1 small onion, peeled and finely chopped

1 garlic clove, peeled and finely chopped or crushed

1 tsp fresh ginger, very finely grated

1 tsp ground coriander

1 tsp ground cumin

1 large can brown lentils, drained

1 courgette, very finely grated (optional)

1 tbsp breadcrumbs or 1 tbsp gram or plain flour

1 tbsp fresh parsley or mint leaves, finely chopped

squeeze of lime juice

plenty of salt and freshly ground black pepper

To serve

4 flatbreads or pitta breads

spicy yoghurt sauce (see page 113) or homemade ketchup (see page 164)

Method

Bring a saucepan of salted water to the boil, turn down to a simmer and cook the sweet potato for 10–15 minutes until tender.

Meanwhile, in a small pan gently sauté the onion in the sunflower oil for about 3 minutes until soft. Add the garlic, ginger, coriander and cumin and stir around with the onion for about 30 seconds.

When the sweet potato is cooked, drain well and transfer to a mixing bowl. Add the onion mix plus the rest of the burger ingredients and mash roughly with a fork.

Using your hands, shape the mixture into four equal-sized burgers. Chill in the fridge for 30 minutes to allow the burgers to firm up and the flavours to infuse.

Preheat a griddle or frying pan to hot and then cook the burgers for about 3 minutes each side until just cooked through, turning just once. Warm the pitta bread, cut a slit lengthways and stuff with the burger and sauce.

Nutrition per serving

Energy	Protein	Carbs	Sugars
408kcal	**16.5g**	**80g**	**8g**
Salt	Fibre	Fat	Saturates
2.1g	**6g**	**3.5g**	**0.5g**

Spicy Sweetcorn Fritters

Prep 5 mins Cook 5 mins

Corn is packed with goodness to give young athletes a boost.

Sweet and delicious, corn is surprisingly nutrient-rich, loaded with carotenoids, which fight infection and promote healthy eyesight, hair and skin, as well as carbohydrate, fibre, vitamin C and manganese. These fritters tend to be a hit with all ages.

Ingredients for 12 fritters

1 large, free-range egg

1 large can sweetcorn, drained (about 280g)

2 tbsp creamed canned sweetcorn

2 spring onions, finely chopped

½ tsp green chilli, finely chopped (optional)

½ tsp ground cumin

¼–½ tsp salt and a few grinds of black pepper

zest of one lime

25g fresh coriander leaves, roughly chopped

2 tbsp gram (chickpea) flour or plain flour

1 tbsp rapeseed or sunflower oil for frying

ketchup or chilli sauce for dipping

Method

Break the egg into a mixing bowl and lightly whisk with a fork. Add the sweetcorn, the creamed sweetcorn, spring onions, chilli, cumin, seasoning, lime zest, coriander and flour. Stir until well combined.

Heat the oil in a heavy-based frying pan over a medium heat. Dollop tablespoons of the mixture into the pan and cook for a few minutes on each side until they are golden brown and cooked through.

Remove with a slice and place onto a piece of kitchen towel to soak up any excess oil.

Serve with homemade ketchup (see page 164) or chilli sauce.

Delicious served with chopped avocado and crispy bacon, grilled chicken or lamb chops!

Nutrition per serving

Energy	Protein	Carbs	Sugars
43kcal	1.4g	6.2g	0.9g

Salt	Fibre	Fat	Saturates
0.4g	0.7g	1.8g	-

Lemon Butter Salmon Parcels

Prep 5 mins Cook 12 mins

Unwrap these parcels to discover mouth-wateringly tender fillets of fish with an aromatic buttery lemon sauce.

Oily fish is not only packed with heart-healthy omega-3's, it also contains the full spectrum of amino acids necessary for the growth and maintenance of lean muscle tissue. Very convenient for evenings when members of the family arrive home hungry at different times, prepare these parcels in advance, refrigerate and then cook as needed.

Ingredients to serve 4

40g unsalted butter

zest and juice of one small lemon

1 tbsp dill, tarragon or parsley (or a mix of all three), finely chopped

sea salt flakes and freshly ground black pepper

4 salmon fillets (about 125g each)

4 pieces of baking parchment or greaseproof paper, cut into 25 x 20cm rectangles

Method

Preheat the oven to 180°C/gas mark 4.

In a small bowl, combine the butter with the herbs, lemon zest, salt and pepper.

Place each salmon fillet in the middle of the baking parchment and then place ¼ of the butter mixture onto each fillet. Pour a little lemon juice over each fillet.

Fold the parchment paper lengthways into envelopes around the fish, folding the end flaps underneath the parcel to secure.

Bake in the oven for 10 minutes, 12 minutes if you've made the parcels in advance and you are transferring them straight from the fridge to the oven.

Serve the parcels on individual plates, allowing each person to unwrap their own package.

Serve with brown basmati rice and steamed tender stem broccoli for a fabulously healthy training meal.

Nutrition per serving

Energy	Protein	Carbs	Sugars
303kcal	23g	0g	0g

Salt	Fibre	Fat	Saturates
1.3g	0g	23g	8g

Honey Glazed Mackerel Fillet

Prep 2 mins Cook 15 mins

A tasty fish dish that is good for the body and good for the brain.

A deliciously sweet-sour sticky sauce complements the rich, oily texture of the mackerel. Served with stir-fried vegetables and egg noodles or brown basmati rice, this meal is extremely nutritious and well balanced.

Ingredients to serve 4

1 tsp sunflower or olive oil to oil the dish

2 tbsp honey or maple syrup

2 tbsp lime juice

zest of 1 lime

1 tbsp light soy sauce

1 tsp light brown sugar

1 tsp fresh ginger, peeled and finely grated (optional)

4 mackerel fillets

1 tbsp spring onions, finely sliced (optional)

1 tbsp fresh coriander, roughly chopped, for garnish (optional)

Method

Preheat the oven to 200°C/gas mark 6 and brush an ovenproof dish lightly with the oil.

In a small bowl, combine the honey, lime juice and zest, soy sauce, sugar and ginger.

Dip each piece of mackerel into the sauce and lay onto the dish, skin side down if the mackerel still has its skin on. Spoon over any remaining sauce.

Bake in the oven for 10–12 minutes, or until the mackerel is just cooked, basting the fish with the sauce halfway through the cooking time.

Transfer each fish fillet onto a warmed plate and spoon over any excess sauce, sprinkle over a little spring onion and coriander garnish, if you like.

Nutrition per serving

Energy	Protein		Carbs	Sugars
402kcal	**29g**		**10g**	**9.5g**
Salt	Fibre		Fat	Saturates
0.9g	**0.5g**		**27g**	**5g**

Mains

Prepare & Cook in under 45 Minutes

Spaghetti with Pork and Apple Meatballs, Roasted Red Pepper Sauce

Prep 30 mins Cook 15 mins

Mouth-watering and sustaining, this family meal will support a healthy immune system.

Brimming with vitamins A, B6, C and E and the anti-carcinogenic lycopene, along with dietary fibre and potassium, the colourful red pepper sauce adds a massive nutritional punch to this flavoursome dish, which has an excellent balance of low-GI carbohydrate, protein and fat.

Ingredients for 4 large portions

400g spaghetti

For the sauce
4 red peppers, sliced in half, seeds removed

1 tbsp olive oil

1 small onion, peeled and finely chopped

1 bay leaf (optional)

1 small garlic clove (optional)

400g can of chopped tomatoes

salt and freshly ground black pepper

For the meatballs
500g pork mince, preferably good-quality organic

40g wholemeal breadcrumbs

2 medium apples, peeled, cored and grated

1 small red chilli, seeds removed and very finely chopped

½ onion, peeled and grated

1 scant tsp fennel seeds, crushed into a powder in a pestle and mortar (use mixed herbs or oregano as an alternative)

plenty of salt and freshly ground black pepper

1 tbsp olive oil to fry

Nutrition per serving

Energy	Protein	Carbs	Sugars
681kcal	48g	89g	19g

Salt	Fibre	Fat	Saturates
1.5g	7g	15g	3g

Method

Heat the oven to 200°C/gas mark 6. Place the red peppers on a lightly oiled baking tray, skin side upwards and roast for 30 minutes, until the skin is wrinkly and slightly charred. Remove from the oven. Peel off the skin and chop roughly. Reserve any juices from the baking tray.

Meanwhile, combine the pork mince, breadcrumbs, grated apple and onion, chilli, fennel and salt and pepper in a large bowl.

Form small meatballs with your hands, 1–2cm in diameter. Pile onto a plate and refrigerate while you make the sauce and the spaghetti.

For the sauce, heat 1 tbsp olive oil in a saucepan. Add the onion and bay leaf, stir, cover with a lid and cook very gently for about 10 minutes until translucent and soft. Add the garlic, tomatoes, red peppers, the reserved pepper juices and season with salt and pepper.

Bring a large pan of salted water to the boil and cook the spaghetti according to pack instructions.

Meanwhile, heat a tbsp of olive oil in a large non-stick frying pan and fry the meatballs in batches over a medium heat for a few minutes on each side until they are golden and just cooked through (break one open to check).

Drain the spaghetti, return it to the pan with a small ladleful of the cooking water to prevent it sticking. Divide the spaghetti onto four warmed pasta plates, add the meatballs and pour over the sauce.

Rigatoni with Butternut Squash, Pancetta and Thyme

Prep 10 mins Cook 20 mins

Comforting and delicious, this dish provides outstanding levels of antioxidants.

Low GI and highly nutritious, this tasty meal is rich in carbohydrate and the antioxidant and anti-inflammatory beta-carotene (vitamin A), as well as vitamin C, iron, potassium and fibre, plus folic acid, vitamin B1 and omega-3 fatty acids.

Ingredients to serve 4

1 butternut squash, peeled, deseeded and diced into cubes

400g rigatoni

1 tbsp olive oil

1 garlic clove, very finely sliced

8 slices pancetta

1 tsp fresh thyme (the leaves of about 3 sprigs), plus extra to serve

2 tbsp half-fat crème fraîche

salt and freshly ground black pepper

grated Parmesan to serve

Method

Bring a large pan of salted water to the boil. Add the butternut squash and cook until very tender. Drain when cooked, reserving a good ladleful of the cooking water, and set aside.

Bring another large pan of salted water to the boil and cook the rigatoni according to pack instructions until al dente.

Meanwhile, heat the olive oil in a frying pan and very gently sauté the garlic until soft. Remove and add to the butternut squash.

Add the pancetta to the frying pan and cook until crisp. Remove and lay out on some kitchen paper to soak up any excess fat.

Turn the heat to low and add the butternut squash and garlic to the frying pan, then the thyme, crème fraîche and a little freshly ground black pepper. Mash it all up with a fork until creamy.

Add the cooked pasta and the reserved cooking water to the butternut squash sauce. Carefully combine and then serve on warmed pasta dishes with 2 slices of pancetta laid on top of each serving, a few more sprinklings of fresh thyme and some grated Parmesan.

Nutrition per serving

Energy	Protein	Carbs	Sugars
545kcal	**22g**	**97g**	**8g**

Salt	Fibre	Fat	Saturates
0.9g	**7.4g**	**12.8g**	**4g**

Sweet and Sour Chicken with Basmati Rice

Prep 10 mins Cook 15 mins

Kids will love this speedy meal, with an excellent balance of protein and low-GI carbs for sustained energy and healthy muscles.

Eating a spectrum of different-coloured foods provides the best variety of immunity-boosting phytonutrients, vitamins and trace minerals, all-important nutrients to help the body grow and stay healthy. Crammed with reds, yellows and greens, this recipe is definitely on the colourful side!

Ingredients to serve 4

400g basmati rice

For the sweet and sour sauce

2 tbsp soft brown sugar

4 tbsp white wine or rice wine vinegar

454g can pineapple chunks in juice

2 heaped tbsp tomato ketchup

2 tbsp soy sauce

3cm fresh ginger, peeled and grated

1 clove garlic, peeled and finely sliced

For the chicken

1 tbsp cornflour or flour

1 tsp salt

1 tsp five-spice powder

400g skinless, boneless chicken thighs

2 tbsp sunflower or rapeseed oil

4 spring onions, cut into 3cm lengths

1 red, 1 yellow and 1 green pepper, deseeded and cut into chunks

25g fresh coriander, roughly chopped (optional)

Method

Cook the rice according to the pack instructions.

In a small saucepan dissolve the sugar in the vinegar over a gentle heat. Add the pineapple juice and chunks, tomato ketchup and soy sauce. Bring to the boil. Add the ginger and garlic and simmer for a few minutes until the sauce starts to thicken. Set aside.

Combine the cornflour, salt and five spice on a plate. Cut the chicken into 2cm cubes and toss it around in the flour mix to coat thoroughly.

Preheat a wok or large, heavy-based frying pan to very hot. Add 1 tbsp of the oil and quickly fry the chicken in batches. Turn the pieces around so that the chicken becomes brown and crisp all over. This should take a few minutes per batch. Lift the chicken out and set aside.

Take the wok off the heat, quickly wipe clean with a piece of kitchen towel and return to a high heat. Add another tbsp oil and stir fry the spring onions and peppers for a few minutes until just tender – you want them to retain their crunch.

Add the chicken and the sauce to the vegetables. Stir to combine. Sprinkle with fresh coriander, if you like, and serve with the basmati rice.

Nutrition per serving

Energy	Protein	Carbs	Sugars
750kcal	29.5g	125g	35g

Salt	Fibre	Fat	Saturates
3g	4.5g	15.5g	3.5g

Chicken Mango Fajitas with Salsa

Prep 10 mins Cook 15 mins

Fajitas, packed with carbohydrate, protein and a good spectrum of vitamins, make a healthy low-fat meal for athletic kids.

I'll often prepare fajitas when my children have friends to visit. Kids can assemble their own wraps, picking the fillings they like. It's funny to see them stuff their wraps so full that the whole thing falls apart! Use shop-bought guacamole and tzatziki dips if you've no time to prepare your own salsa.

Ingredients to serve 4

For the chicken

2 free-range chicken breasts, skin on

4 tortilla wraps

2 large handfuls of rocket or watercress

glug of balsamic vinegar

fresh coriander leaves to serve

For the marinade

2 tbsp mango chutney

½ tbsp madras curry paste

1 tsp each ground coriander and ground cumin

1 tbsp olive oil

1 tbsp lemon juice

For the salsa

1 avocado, not too ripe, peeled and diced

6cm cucumber, diced into small cubes

6 cherry tomatoes, chopped into quarters

handful of fresh coriander leaves, chopped

juice of ½ a lime

1 tbsp olive oil

For the spicy yoghurt sauce

200ml low-fat natural yoghurt

pinch of chilli powder

½ tsp each ground coriander and ground cumin

Method

Combine the marinade ingredients in a dish with the chicken, cover and refrigerate for 1-24 hours. Mix together the yoghurt sauce ingredients in a small bowl, cover and chill. Combine all the salsa ingredients in a bowl, cover and chill.

Place the chicken in a small baking tray. Heat the grill to high and grill for 10–15 minutes, skin side up, coating frequently with the marinade. Turn halfway through cooking, then turn skin side up again to crisp up for the last couple of minutes.

Meanwhile, wrap the tortilla wraps in foil and warm in the oven.

Transfer the chicken to a plate and carve into diagonal strips. Discard any fat in the baking tray, add a glug of balsamic vinegar and scrape off any tasty bits stuck to the sides. Pour over the chicken. Decorate with coriander leaves.

Place the wraps, salsa, yoghurt sauce, chicken and rocket on the table. Everyone can add a little of what they fancy to each tortilla, roll it up, cut it in half, pick it up and eat it.

Nutrition per serving

Energy	Protein	Carbs	Sugars
700kcal	**36g**	**60g**	**43g**
Salt	Fibre	Fat	Saturates
1.7g	**7g**	**38g**	**10g**

Pork Tenderloin and Chorizo Kebabs

Prep 10 mins Cook 10–15 mins

Served with couscous and salad, these kebabs make a balanced nutrient-rich plate of carbs, protein and healthy fats.

Chorizo is pretty high in cholesterol, but used sparingly, it adds a wonderful depth of flavour. Buy chorizo in its whole 'sausage' form rather than sliced – it is usually in a pack on the shelf with other pre-packed whole salamis in the supermarket.

Ingredients to serve 4

8 metal or bamboo skewers

For the marinade
6 tbsp olive oil

juice of 1 lemon

12 sage leaves, whole

1 tsp paprika

salt and pepper

For the kebabs
2 x 175–200g tenderloins of pork, fat removed, cut into 12 x 2.5cm cubes

2 green peppers

24 sage leaves

24 x 2cm cubes bread (granary best)

1 chorizo sausage cut into 12 x 2cm pieces

Method

If you are using bamboo skewers, soak them in a bowl of water for 30 minutes or so before using them so that they don't burn when you cook the kebabs.

In a bowl, mix together the marinade ingredients. Add the kebab ingredients and make sure everything is well coated.

Thread the kebabs in the following order: green pepper, pork, sage leaf, bread, chorizo, green pepper, pork, sage leaf, bread etc.

Heat the griddle, grill or barbecue to a medium heat and cook the kebabs for about 10 minutes, turning so that all the sides get cooked. The bread should go crispy and the pork should be just cooked through.

Thread the bread next to the chorizo so that the juices run into it – delicious!

Nutrition per serving

Energy	Protein	Carbs	Sugars
650kcal	38g	26g	8g

Salt	Fibre	Fat	Saturates
1.1g	4g	39g	9g

Sticky Lemon Honey Chicken with Basmati, Wild and Chickpea Rice

Prep 5 mins Cook 30 mins

This traybake supper may be balanced and extremely nutritious, but we love it because it minimises on washing-up.

The chickpeas not only add bulk to satisfy hungry kids and sustain energy levels, they're also a great source of minerals and fibre and a virtually fat-free source of protein. Don't worry too much about accurate measurements; you'll still end up with delicious, succulent results.

Ingredients to serve 4

8 free-range, bone-in chicken thighs or combo of thighs and drumsticks, skin on

1 scant tbsp olive oil

2 tbsp honey

2 tbsp lemon juice

1 garlic clove, crushed

½ tbsp balsamic vinegar

1 tsp mixed Italian herbs

1 tsp ras-el-hanout spice mix

a little chilli sauce (optional)

salt and freshly ground black pepper

400g basmati and wild rice

400g can of chickpeas, drained (optional)

Method

Preheat the oven to 190°C/gas mark 5.

Mix together the olive oil, honey, lemon juice, garlic, vinegar, herbs, spices and chilli sauce, if using. Place the chicken thighs in a roasting dish, skin side up – it is best if they fit in quite tightly – and coat with the honey mixture. Sprinkle with a little salt and black pepper. You might want to fit in the remains of the squeezed lemon halves to add a little flavour – they caramelise nicely when they are roasted.

Place in the oven and roast for 30–40 minutes, until the chicken is cooked and the skins are sticky, golden and caramelised.

Meanwhile, cook the rice according to pack instructions – basmati and wild rice normally take about 25 minutes. Stir the chickpeas into the rice once it is cooked.

Serve on warmed plates, spooning over any extra juices from the roasting tin.

Nutrition per serving

Energy	Protein	Carbs	Sugars
670kcal	33g	108.5g	8g

Salt	Fibre	Fat	Saturates
1.2g	5g	14.5g	3.5g

Serve with a colourful and crunchy rainbow salad (see page 168).

Fish Pie with Cheese, Bacon and Breadcrumb Topping

Prep 8 mins Cook 20 mins

Comforting, nutrient-rich and packed with low-fat protein.

This no-fuss fish pie makes a sustaining, low-GI training meal served with fresh green beans and baby new potatoes. You could pack in even more nutrients by adding a layer of gently sautéed sliced leeks, courgettes or mushrooms before sprinkling over the topping.

Ingredients to serve 4

500g skinless white fish, such as haddock, hake, cod, coley, or a mix of white fish and raw prawns

500ml milk

1 bay leaf

5 peppercorns

salt and freshly ground black pepper

50g butter

40g plain flour

pinch of nutmeg

1 tsp of coarse-grain mustard

1 tsp olive oil

4 rashers smoked bacon, finely chopped

4 heaped tbsp fresh breadcrumbs (shop-bought is fine)

25g fresh curly parsley, finely chopped (optional)

50g cheddar cheese or Parmesan, grated

Method

Preheat the oven to 200°C/gas mark 6.

Place the fish in a large frying pan, cover with the milk, add the bay leaf, peppercorns and a pinch of salt and slowly bring to the boil. Simmer for 3 minutes, until the fish is partially cooked.

Transfer the fish to a 20 x 30cm baking dish. Strain the milk into a jug.

Melt the butter in a non-stick saucepan. Add the flour and stir for a minute, over a very low heat. Remove the pan from the heat, then slowly beat in the milk, stirring all the time to prevent lumps forming. Return to the heat and gradually bring to a gentle simmer, stirring until the sauce becomes thick and glossy. Add the nutmeg, mustard and seasoning, then pour over the fish.

Clean the frying pan and, over a medium heat, fry the bacon for a couple of minutes in a drop of oil, until crisp. Take off the heat, stir in the breadcrumbs, parsley, if using, and cheese. Spoon over the fish mixture to cover it completely. Bake for 20 minutes, until the top is a crisp, golden brown.

Buy packs of mixed fish from the fishmongers or supermarket to store in the freezer.

Nutrition per serving

Energy	Protein	Carbs	Sugars
570kcal	36.5g	21.5g	6.5g
Salt	Fibre	Fat	Saturates
3g	1.5g	30g	13g

Indian-style Salmon, Sag Aloo and Cucumber Raita

Prep 10 mins Cook 20 mins

Every delicious mouthful of this meal is packed with goodness!

Spinach and salmon in one meal; excellent for boosting energy, keeping nasty viruses at bay and promoting post-exercise recovery. Spices are packed with minerals and antioxidants to control blood sugar levels, protect against inflammation and reduce susceptibility to diseases such as heart disease and type 2 diabetes.

Ingredients to serve 4

For the salmon

1 tbsp sunflower or rapeseed oil

1 tsp each ground cumin, ground coriander and garam masala

½ tsp salt

4 salmon fillets

1 lime cut into quarters to serve

Cucumber raita

250g natural yoghurt

½ cucumber, grated

handful of fresh mint (optional)

pinch of salt

For the sag aloo

400g potatoes, peeled and cut into 2cm chunks

1 tbsp sunflower oil

1 tsp black mustard seeds

1 onion, peeled and finely sliced

1 tsp garam masala

1 tsp turmeric

2cm piece of fresh ginger, peeled and grated

2 garlic cloves, peeled and finely sliced

1 red chilli, deseeded and finely sliced

½ tsp salt, or to taste

400g can chopped tomatoes or 4 fresh tomatoes, chopped

100ml vegetable stock

250g bag of spinach

25g coriander, roughly chopped (optional)

Nutrition per serving

Energy	Protein	Carbs	Sugars
509kcal	**38g**	**31g**	**13g**
Salt	Fibre	Fat	Saturates
2.5g	**6g**	**25g**	**4.5g**

Method

Preheat the oven to 180°C/gas mark 4.

Combine the oil, cumin, coriander, garam masala and salt. Arrange the salmon on a plate, coat with the spice combination and leave to marinate while you prepare the sag aloo and raita.

Make the raita: squeeze out any excess water from the cucumber and combine with the yoghurt, mint and salt in a small bowl.

Parboil the potatoes in salted water for 5 minutes and then drain them. Heat the oil in a frying pan, add the mustard seeds and, on a medium heat, cook for 20–30 seconds until they start to pop. Add the onion, and gently sauté on a low heat for about 3 minutes. Stir in the potatoes, the garam masala, turmeric, ginger, garlic, red chilli and salt. Sauté for another minute, stirring frequently, so the potatoes are nicely covered with the spices.

Add the tomatoes and vegetable stock, cover and simmer for about 8 minutes, or until the potatoes are just cooked through and have soaked up the stock. Stir in the spinach and coriander until the spinach wilts. Taste for seasoning.

Meanwhile, heat a heavy-based ovenproof frying pan (no oil required) to a medium heat and add the salmon fillets, laying them skin side down. Cook for a couple of minutes, until sealed, and then turn to seal each side. This should take 3–4 minutes. Place the frying pan in the oven and finish cooking in the oven for a further 5 minutes, or until the salmon is just cooked through, that is, when it is just a little springy to the touch.

Serve the salmon, the sag aloo and cucumber raita on warmed plates with a wedge of lime each to squeeze over.

Fresh Go Faster Gnocchi

Prep 25 mins Cook 5 mins

Warming, filling, nourishing; feather-light gnocchi makes a great recovery lunch for active children on a cold winter's day.

You can buy good pre-prepared gnocchi, admittedly, but it's good fun, if a little messy, to get the kids to help and make your own! Work quickly and carefully, as you would with pastry, to achieve the lightest results.

Ingredients to serve 4

500g floury potatoes (such as King Edward's)

1 large, free-range egg, lightly beaten

150g plain flour (Italian '00 is best)

½ tsp salt

freshly ground black pepper

olive oil to serve

Toss gnocchi with homemade pesto (see page 166) or extra virgin olive oil, Parmesan shavings and freshly ground black pepper.

Method

Boil the potatoes in their skins in salted water for about 25 minutes, or until tender. Drain and, when cool enough to handle, carefully remove the peel with a sharp knife.

Mash or grate the potatoes, or mince in a potato ricer. Stir in the egg, flour, salt and plenty of black pepper.

Bring the mixture together with your hands into a ball and, on a floured surface, gently knead it, like dough, until soft and not too sticky. Divide into sections and roll each section into a sausage shape. Using a sharp knife, cut into little gnocchi (flattish oval balls), about 1–1½ cm in length and put them into a floured container. They are now ready to cook, or if you like, you can keep them for 2–3 days, chilled, in the floured container.

Bring a large saucepan of salted water to a gentle simmer and cook the gnocchi in batches, a handful at a time, for about 2 minutes, or until they rise to the surface.

Remove with a slotted spoon and serve immediately.

Nutrition per serving

Energy	Protein	Carbs	Sugars
269kcal	**7g**	**48g**	**1.6g**
Salt	Fibre	Fat	Saturates
0.7g	**4g**	**5g**	**1g**

Roasted Butternut Squash Risotto with Maple Syrup Almonds

Prep 5 mins Cook 25 mins

Quick, tasty and good value; a great midweek meal for active kids and adults alike.

A Go Faster Food favourite of 2012 Team GB Olympian marathon runner Claire Hallissey, this delicious combo of nutrient-rich butternut squash, risotto rice, almonds and Parmesan is quick to cook, healthy and sustaining. Replace the butternut with higher-GI pumpkin to transform this into an effective recovery meal.

Ingredients to serve 4

1 butternut squash, peeled, seeds removed and cut into 2cm cubes

2 tbsp olive oil

salt and freshly ground black pepper

small handful of flaked almonds

1 tbsp maple syrup, diluted with a few drops of water

3 knobs of butter

1 onion, peeled and finely sliced

1 garlic clove, peeled and crushed

350g risotto rice (Vialone Nano or Arborio)

225ml dry white wine (optional, could use extra stock instead)

1¼–1½ litres hot vegetable or chicken stock

1 tsp saffron strands (optional)

75g freshly grated Parmesan

Method

Preheat the oven to 200°C/gas mark 6.

Put the squash on a baking tray, toss it with 1 tbsp olive oil, then sprinkle with salt and black pepper. Roast in the oven for 25 minutes or until the squash is tender and golden; stir occasionally.

Meanwhile mix the almonds with the maple syrup and water and bake on a baking tray in the oven for about 5 minutes until crisp.

Melt 2 knobs of butter with the remaining olive oil in a large heavy-based pan. Gently sauté the onion until it becomes translucent, then add the garlic and sauté for a few minutes. Add the rice and stir until the grains become translucent and glossy. Stir in the wine and cook for a few minutes until completely absorbed. Stir in the saffron then add the hot stock, a ladle at a time, stirring slowly but constantly. Make sure each ladleful is absorbed by the rice before adding the next. Depending on the rice, you may need a little more or less stock.

After 18–20 minutes, when the rice is tender and creamy, turn off the heat. Taste for seasoning, and stir in the Parmesan, butternut squash and butter. Let the mixture stand for a couple of minutes. Serve with the almonds and more Parmesan.

Nutrition per serving

Energy	Protein	Carbs	Sugars
689kcal	**18g**	**104g**	**12g**
Salt	Fibre	Fat	Saturates
1.7g	**4g**	**22g**	**8g**

Risi e Bisi

Prep 2 mins Cook 20 mins

Rice and peas, there's little not to like about this classic, simple risotto.

Perfect for a quick-and-easy midweek meal, this comforting Italian nursery food tastes absolutely delicious with a green side salad, tossed in a light balsamic dressing and scattered with crispy pancetta. You can adapt this risotto by adding other summer vegetables such as courgettes or broad beans.

Ingredients to serve 4

1¼–1½ litres vegetable stock

60g unsalted butter

1 onion, peeled and finely sliced

1 celery stick, finely chopped

1 garlic clove, peeled and crushed

350g Arborio risotto rice

225ml white wine (optional, could use extra stock instead)

500g frozen peas, defrosted

100g freshly grated Parmesan

salt and freshly ground black pepper

a little grated nutmeg

25g flat-leaf parsley, roughly chopped

Method

Heat up the stock in a saucepan.

Melt 50g of the butter in a large heavy-based pan and gently sauté the onion until it becomes translucent. Add the garlic and celery and sauté for a couple of minutes. Add the rice and stir until the grains become translucent and glossy. Stir in the wine and cook for a couple of minutes until completely absorbed. Add the hot stock, a ladle at a time, stirring slowly but constantly. Make sure each ladleful of stock is absorbed by the rice before adding the next. You may need a little more or less stock, depending on the type of rice you use.

After 18–20 minutes, when the rice is cooked, stir in the peas. The risotto should look nice and creamy, not too soupy, not too solid. Taste to see if you need more salt, turn off the heat, stir in the Parmesan, the nutmeg, the parsley and the rest of the butter. Let the mixture stand for a couple of minutes.

Serve in warmed bowls with some fresh Parmesan shavings.

Nutrition per serving

Energy	Protein	Carbs	Sugars
723kcal	**25.5g**	**91g**	**6g**
Salt	Fibre	Fat	Saturates
2g	**9.5g**	**18g**	**11.5g**

Mains

Slow Cook

Conchiglioni with Roasted Tomato Sauce

Prep 5 mins Cook 60 mins

Low in fat and light on the stomach, this meal is a favourite for before a big match or tournament.

Slow-roasted tomato sauce, deep and intense in flavour, is rich in vitamin C, vitamin A and B vitamins (niacin and riboflavin), magnesium, phosphorous, calcium and fibre, and a fantastic source of the disease-fighting antioxidant lycopene.

Ingredients to serve 4

8 medium vine tomatoes, halved

1 tbsp balsamic vinegar

2 tbsp olive oil

1 tsp Demerara sugar

plenty of salt and freshly ground black pepper

2 garlic cloves, peeled and crushed

½ bottle sugocasa or passata

1 small dried chilli, flaked (optional)

bunch of fresh basil, chopped, saving a few leaves whole for decoration

4 rashers streaky bacon or prosciutto (optional)

500g Conchiglioni pasta shells

1 tsp olive oil to drizzle over pasta

Parmesan shavings to serve

Method

Preheat the oven to 180°C/gas mark 4.

Place the tomatoes cut side up on a baking tray. Sprinkle with the balsamic vinegar, olive oil, sugar, salt and pepper and cook for 30–40 minutes, until the tomatoes are soft and slightly caramelised. Scatter with garlic 5 minutes before removing the tomatoes from the oven.

Transfer to a saucepan, scraping off any caramelised bits. Stir in the sugocasa or passata and chilli, if using. Cover and cook very gently for 20 minutes, stirring frequently. Taste for seasoning, adding more balsamic vinegar, olive oil, salt or pepper if needed. Add the basil.

Grill the bacon until really crispy.

Meanwhile, cook the pasta shells in a large pan of salted water, according to pack instructions. Drain, reserving a ladleful of cooking liquid to prevent the pasta sticking. Drizzle with olive oil and toss together with the sauce.

Serve in warmed bowls with a slice of bacon on top of each serving. Scatter with basil leaves and Parmesan shavings.

Kids eat individual sauce-filled Conchiglioni with their hands, popping them, whole, into their mouths. Messy but worth it!

Nutrition per serving

Energy	Protein		Carbs	Sugars
639kcal	22g		100g	12g
Salt	Fibre		Fat	Saturates
1.8g	6g		19g	6g

Smoky Black Bean and Chorizo Chilli with Salsa

Prep 15 mins (+ overnight soaking for dried beans) Cook 1½ hours

Wholesome and packed with complex carbs, protein, B vitamins, iron and calcium to fuel training, this is no ordinary chilli!

Chris Edwards of rock band Kasabian popped in for a Go Faster Food supper in Bristol whilst cycling from Land's End to John O'Groats with his brother, Jason. Fuelled by this chilli and some Go Faster chocolate brownies, their ride the following day was apparently the best ever!

Ingredients to serve 4

For the smoky chilli

400g stewing beef, chopped into fairly small chunks (1cm)

2 tbsp flour mixed with ¼ tsp each salt, pepper and cayenne pepper

2 tbsp olive oil

100g spicy chorizo chopped into 1cm chunks

1 onion, peeled and finely sliced

2 green peppers, deseeded and chopped into 1cm chunks

1 bay leaf

1 tsp smoked paprika

1 large garlic clove, peeled and crushed

100g black beans, rinsed and soaked overnight, then rinsed again and drained

500ml chicken stock

400g can chopped tomatoes

salt and freshly ground black pepper

handful of coriander leaves, chopped

squeeze of lime juice

1 green chilli, finely sliced and with seeds remaining, or two if you like it really hot

rice and soured cream (optional) to serve

For the salsa

½ small cucumber, diced

1 avocado, peeled and diced

10 cherry tomatoes, quartered

4 spring onions, finely sliced

1 tsp coriander seeds, crushed in pestle and mortar

handful of mint leaves, roughly chopped

handful of coriander leaves, roughly chopped

juice of 1 lime

glug of olive oil

Gram for gram, black beans contain 10 times more antioxidants than oranges!

Nutrition per serving

Energy	Protein	Carbs	Sugars
534kcal	38g	36g	12g
Salt	Fibre	Fat	Saturates
2g	8g	27g	4g

Method

Preheat the oven to 160°C/gas mark 3.

Toss the beef chunks in the flour mix. Heat 1 tbsp oil in a flameproof casserole dish and brown the beef in batches. Set aside. Brown the chorizo and set aside too. Scrape the juices off the bottom of the pan using a splash of water and pour over the beef.

Add the remaining oil and gently sauté the onion and green peppers with the bay leaf for a few minutes. Stir in the smoked paprika, beef, chorizo, garlic, black beans, stock and tinned tomatoes and bring everything to the boil. Give it a good stir, cover and transfer to the oven to gently cook for 1½ hours until the beef and the beans are tender and the sauce has become nice and thick. Add salt and pepper now, according to taste. If you are making the dish in advance, cool and chill, and carry out the following stages just before you serve.

Stir in the coriander and lime juice. Taste and add more salt, pepper or smoked paprika if you like.

Make the salsa just before serving, by combining all the salsa ingredients in a bowl.

Serve the chilli in bowls with rice, salsa, and a dollop of soured cream. Offer chopped green chillies on the side for those who like it really hot.

Chilli Chocolate Chicken

Prep 10 mins Cook 70 mins

Dark, sweet, spicy and packed with antioxidants to supercharge energy levels.

Kids who like chilli con carne will love this chilli chocolate chicken, based on the Mexican 'mole'. A traditional mole uses a massive array of ingredients and different varieties of chilli. This Go Faster streamlined version certainly doesn't skimp on flavour but does involve much less shopping. Serve with brown basmati rice or quinoa.

Ingredients to serve 4

2 dried chillies (or to taste)

50g raisins

8 free-range bone-in chicken thighs

salt and freshly ground black pepper

2 tbsp coconut or sunflower oil

2 onions, peeled and finely sliced

1 cinnamon stick

2 tsp each ground coriander and ground cumin

¼ tsp ground cloves

3 garlic cloves, peeled and crushed

1 heaped tbsp peanut, cashew or almond butter

1 tsp chilli paste (optional)

zest of ½ an orange

400g can of chopped tomatoes

500ml chicken stock

25g dark chocolate (at least 70% cocoa solids)

juice of one lime

25g fresh coriander, roughly chopped,

soured cream and lime wedges to serve

Method

Put the chillies and raisins in a small bowl, cover with boiling water and leave for 10 minutes.

Season the chicken. Heat 1 tbsp oil in a flameproof casserole dish and brown the chicken, turning frequently to seal all over. Remove and set aside. Add another 1 tbsp oil to the casserole and sauté the onions until soft and translucent. Stir in the cinnamon stick, coriander, cumin and cloves and cook for 1 minute. Return the chicken and take off the heat.

Blend the chillies, raisins and soaking water, or bash with a pestle and mortar. Add this to the casserole with the garlic, nut butter, chilli paste, if using, orange zest and tomatoes. Pour in enough stock to cover everything. Return the casserole to the heat and bring to the boil.

Cover, reduce to a simmer, and cook for 45 minutes or until the sauce is thick and the chicken is cooked through. Add the chocolate and continue to cook, uncovered, on a low heat for another 15 minutes. If the sauce is too thick, add more stock or water. Stir in the lime juice and check for seasoning.

Sprinkle with coriander and serve with a dollop of soured cream and lime wedges.

Nutrition per serving

Energy		Protein		Carbs		Sugars	
388kcal		**25.5g**		**25g**		**21g**	
Salt		Fibre		Fat		Saturates	
1.4g		**4g**		**21g**		**7g**	

Sticky Ribs with Brown Basmati Rice

Prep 5 mins Cook 80 mins

Cheap and always popular, you can't really go wrong with ribs.

Decadent in taste and surprisingly healthy prepared Go Faster Food style, with citrus and fruit juices and served with low-GI brown basmati rice, these ribs make a practical and sustaining weekday training meal.

Ingredients to serve 4

1kg lean pork ribs

500g tomato passata

3 tbsp redcurrant jelly or marmalade

1 tbsp runny honey

1 tbsp soy sauce

1 garlic clove, peeled and crushed

2cm fresh ginger, peeled and finely grated

zest and juice of one lime

zest and juice of one orange

salt and freshly ground black pepper

1 tsp dried thyme

250–300g brown basmati rice

a crunchy cucumber salad to serve

Method

Preheat the oven to 200°C/gas mark 6.

Lay the ribs out on a large roasting dish. In a large bowl, mix together all the rest of the ingredients and pour over the ribs. Cover with foil and bake for about 35 minutes.

Remove the foil and bake the ribs for a further 45 minutes, basting frequently until the ribs are tender and sticky.

Meanwhile, cook the rice according to the instructions on the pack.

Serve the ribs with the rice and a crunchy cucumber salad.

Prepare these ribs in advance and refrigerate for up to 48 hours.

Nutrition per serving

Energy	Protein	Carbs	Sugars
711kcal	**55g**	**84g**	**33g**

Salt	Fibre	Fat	Saturates
1.6g	**3.5g**	**16.5g**	**5.5g**

Spatchcock-roasted Chicken with Grapes

Prep 5 mins Cook 1 hour

Simple but impressive, a super-practical way to roast a chicken.

Kids love a spatchcock-roasted chicken because there is more crispy skin to fight over. Red grapes add a sweet and sour flavour to the sauce. They're a low-GI fruit and are rich in antioxidant vitamins. They also have anti-inflammatory properties, and are great for stabilising blood sugar levels.

Ingredients to serve 4

1 whole free-range chicken (about 1½kg)

2 tbsp olive oil

salt and freshly ground black pepper

1 lemon, cut into thin slices

1 medium shallot, peeled and finely sliced

1 garlic clove, peeled and roughly chopped

2 good-sized sprigs of fresh thyme

200ml chicken stock

200ml pot crème fraîche

bunch of black seedless grapes, halved (about 150g)

Method

Bring the chicken to room temperature. Preheat the oven to 180°C/gas mark 4.

Place the chicken breast side down on a chopping board. Using sharp kitchen scissors, cut up along each side of the backbone and remove it. Open the chicken out, turn it over and press it flat, skin side up on the board.

Rub the chicken all over with 1 tbsp olive oil and season with plenty of salt and pepper. Lay the lemon slices, shallot, garlic and thyme on a flameproof roasting dish, drizzle over another tbsp of olive oil and then place the chicken on top, skin side up. Roast in the oven for 1 hour, or until cooked through.

Transfer the chicken to a carving board while you make the sauce.

Discard the lemon slices and spoon off any excess fat, leaving the meat juices in the roasting dish. Over a high heat, add the stock and let it bubble away until reduced by half. Stir in the crème fraîche and grapes and let the sauce continue to bubble away, stirring frequently, until it thickens.

Carve the chicken into joints and serve on warmed plates with the grape sauce.

Nutrition per serving

Energy	Protein	Carbs	Sugars
530kcal	**60g**	**9.5g**	**9g**
Salt	Fibre	Fat	Saturates
1.6g	**0.5g**	**28g**	**10g**

Mango Chutney Chicken with Caramelised Winter Vegetables

Prep 10 mins Cook 40 mins

An effortless and tasty traybake supper.

Scattering vegetables around any meat roasting in the oven concentrates their sugar content, transforming them into sweet deliciousness, plus great recovery food to replenish depleted glycogen stores and restore tired muscles. Add a can of chickpeas if you want to add a bit of bulk to the dish.

Ingredients to serve 4

4 free-range chicken breasts, or 8 bone-in thighs with skin on

2 tbsp mango chutney

2 tbsp olive oil

2 medium waxy potatoes, washed with skin left on

2 sweet potatoes, peeled and cut into chunks

2 parsnips, peeled and cut into chunks

2 leeks, washed, trimmed, cut into chunks

3 medium red onions, peeled and thickly sliced

1 red pepper

2 whole garlic cloves

1 red chilli, seeds removed and very thinly sliced lengthways

1 lemon, sliced into 4 quarters

1 tsp mixed herbs

1½ tsp ground cumin

sea salt and freshly ground pepper

couscous or brown bread to serve

Method

Preheat the oven to 190°C/gas mark 5.

Spread the skins of the chicken with the mango chutney and set aside on a plate.

Place all the rest of the ingredients into a large roasting dish and mix around with your hands so that all the vegetables are nicely coated with the oil, herbs and spices.

Arrange the chicken pieces over the top of the vegetables, skin side up, and put the roasting dish in the oven.

Bake for about 30–40 minutes, until the chicken is crispy on top and the vegetables are nicely caramelised.

Remove the dish from the oven and serve immediately with couscous or chunks of granary or wholemeal bread to mop up the juices.

Nutrition per serving

Energy	Protein	Carbs	Sugars
440kcal	**32.5g**	**46.5g**	**22g**

Salt	Fibre	Fat	Saturates
1.3g	**10g**	**13g**	**2.5g**

Home-Baked Beans

Prep 5 mins Cook 1½ hours

A simple and nutritious staple to help both stamina and endurance.

Rich in protein, low-GI carbohydrate, B vitamins, fibre and minerals, baked beans are very gradually digested; excellent for keeping hunger at bay and maintaining stable blood glucose levels. The homemade version is extra delicious and even more packed with goodness than the tinned variety.

Ingredients to serve 4

1 tbsp olive oil

1 onion, finely sliced

1 stick celery, finely chopped

1 bay leaf

2 cans haricot, cannellini or borlotti beans, drained

350g tomato passata

2 x 400g cans chopped tomatoes

2 garlic cloves, crushed

2 tsp paprika

2 tsp black treacle

1 tsp muscovado sugar

¼ tsp ground cloves

1 tbsp tomato purée

1 tsp balsamic vinegar

salt and freshly ground black pepper

1 tsp sweet chilli sauce (optional)

handful flat-leaf parsley to serve

Method

Preheat the oven to 150°C/gas mark 2.

In an ovenproof casserole dish, gently sauté the onion and celery with the bay leaf in the olive oil for a few minutes, until soft and translucent. Add 100ml water and then the rest of the ingredients, except the balsamic vinegar, salt, pepper, chilli sauce and parsley, and bring to the boil.

Cover and transfer to the oven. Gently bake for at least 1½ hours, stirring occasionally to scrape the tomato sauce off the sides and into the mixture. You may need to add a little extra water if the juice becomes too thick.

Season well with salt and plenty of black pepper, add the balsamic vinegar and chilli sauce, if using, and sprinkle with parsley to serve.

Try adding some chopped chorizo sausage if you like before the beans go in the oven.

Nutrition per serving

Energy	Protein	Carbs	Sugars
295kcal	**15.5g**	**43.5g**	**20g**
Salt	Fibre	Fat	Saturates
2.9g	**15g**	**4.5g**	**0.5g**

Jamaican Pork and Lentil Stew

Prep 10 mins Cook 60 mins

No great skill is needed for this flavoursome recipe, just a little patience to wait for it to cook.

Green lentils absorb the flavours beautifully when slow-cooked in this sustaining dish, packed with low-GI carbohydrate, fibre, protein, vitamin B1, iron and magnesium. Warming and nourishing, we like to eat this with fresh crusty bread as a pick-me-up on a cold, damp day.

Ingredients to serve 4

2cm piece of fresh ginger, peeled

5 cloves

300g green lentils

1 onion, finely sliced

500g pork belly, cut into 3cm chunks

150g chantenay carrots or carrots cut into 3cm chunks

1 potato, peeled and halved

3 garlic cloves, peeled

400g can chopped tomatoes

¼ tsp each allspice, nutmeg, cayenne pepper, turmeric and cinnamon

1 sprig fresh thyme or 1 tsp dried thyme

1 tsp muscovado sugar

1 tsp red wine vinegar

1 fresh red chilli, whole

1 litre chicken stock, or enough to cover the ingredients by approx. 2cm

salt and freshly ground black pepper

1–2 tbsp lime juice

25g coriander leaves, roughly chopped

crusty bread or couscous to serve

Method

Stud the piece of ginger with the 5 cloves.

Put all the ingredients, except the seasoning, lime juice and coriander leaves, into a flameproof casserole dish. Bring to the boil and boil rapidly, uncovered for 10 minutes, scooping off any frothy scum. Reduce the heat, cover, and simmer for 50 minutes, stirring occasionally, until the lentils are cooked and the sauce looks brown and rich.

With a fork, mash the potato halves and the garlic cloves into the sauce to thicken it up. Remove the clove-studded piece of ginger (and the chilli if you like).

Stir in the lime juice and season. Spoon into warmed bowls, decorate with coriander leaves and serve with crusty bread or plain couscous.

A perfect dish to prepare the day before as the taste will develop and improve overnight.

Nutrition per serving

Energy	Protein	Carbs	Sugars
815kcal	41.5g	55g	10.5g
Salt	Fibre	Fat	Saturates
1.4g	12.5g	39g	12.5g

Cheap and packed with nutrients

Soups are a marvellous vehicle for increasing a young athlete's intake of fresh vegetables. They're also great for disguising ingredients that children may otherwise be sceptical about.

Even the most basic of soups can be extremely tasty; a couple of vegetables simmered together with some chicken stock make a speedy, nutritious and comforting supper. Liven up soups with garlicky croutons, grated cheese or crispy bacon pieces, or bulk them out with pasta, noodles, rice, lentils, chickpeas or butterbeans.

Soups are, of course, tastier and more nutritious made with homemade stock. Just throw left-over cooked or fresh bones in a large saucepan with a couple of carrots, bay leaves, 5 or 6 peppercorns, a stick of celery and a large onion sliced in half. Cover with water, bring to the boil, spoon off any scum that appears on the surface and then simmer, covered, for a couple of hours, perhaps a little longer if you're using fresh bones. Strain the stock, reduce it a little by boiling it down if you like, add salt to taste, and then store it in the fridge or the freezer. For extra delicious stock, brown the bones in some oil on the hob or in a hot oven first. Add the ingredients as above, bring to the boil and cook overnight in the simmering oven of an aga, or at a very low heat in the oven.

Light Meals

Go Faster Soups

Hungarian Goulash Soup

Prep 10 mins (including browning the meat) Cook 1¾ hours

Traditional goulash soup, packed with warming goodness.

Prepare this in advance to return to after a cold morning on the football pitch. Heaven! We eat this soup with chunks of fresh bread, but if you like, reduce the amount of stock and serve as a stew with pasta, rice or gnocchi.

Ingredients to serve 4 (generously)

600g stewing beef or beef chuck steak, cut into small 1cm cubes

2 tbsp plain flour

3 tbsp sunflower oil to brown the meat

1 tbsp red wine vinegar

3–4 medium onions, peeled and diced

2 celery sticks, diced

2 red peppers, deseeded and diced

1 clove garlic, peeled and crushed

2 tbsp sweet Hungarian paprika

1 heaped tsp caraway seeds

1 heaped tsp marjoram or oregano

1 tbsp tomato purée

200g can chopped tomatoes

750ml good beef stock

400g potatoes, peeled and cut into 1cm cubes

salt and freshly ground black pepper

25g fresh flat-leaf parsley, roughly chopped

soured cream to serve (optional)

Nutrition per serving

Energy	Protein	Carbs	Sugars
473kcal	**37.5g**	**41.5g**	**13.5g**

Salt	Fibre	Fat	Saturates
1.5g	**6g**	**17g**	**4g**

Method

Put the flour in a bowl, season with a little salt and black pepper and toss the meat around in it so that it is well covered.

Heat 2 tbsp oil in a large flameproof casserole dish, and brown the beef in small batches. Set aside on a plate.

Add the red wine vinegar and stir it around, scratching any bits of meat stuck to the bottom of the pan and then pour the excess onto the beef.

Add the other tbsp oil and gently sauté the onions, celery and red peppers for a couple of minutes. Add the garlic, cover the pan and leave the vegetables to cook on the lowest heat for about 10 minutes, until soft.

Remove the lid and stir in the paprika, caraway seeds and marjoram, the tomato purée, tomatoes, beef and beef stock. Bring to the boil, then cover and simmer on a gentle heat for at least an hour, until the beef is soft and tender.

Stir in the potatoes and simmer gently for another 30 minutes, until the potatoes are cooked. Season with plenty of salt and pepper and add the flat-leaf parsley.

Serve in warmed soup bowls with a dollop of soured cream and chunks of wholemeal bread.

Leek and Potato Soup

Prep 5 mins Cook 20 mins

This smooth, creamy soup is always a firm favourite.

Simple to make, filling, warming and sustaining for young athletes, this is a great soup to send in a flask for full-day winter tournaments. You'll really notice the difference if you use homemade or good-quality shop-bought stock.

Ingredients to serve 4

25g butter

1 medium onion

3 medium leeks, trimmed, sliced and rinsed in a colander to remove any dirt

3 medium potatoes, peeled and diced

salt and freshly ground black pepper

1–1.2 litres vegetable stock

2 tbsp single cream or crème fraîche

crusty bread to serve

Method

Heat the butter in a large pan and add the onion and leeks. Sweat gently for a few minutes until everything starts to soften, then add the potatoes. Continue to cook very gently for about 5 minutes, stirring frequently.

Season liberally with salt and pepper and then add the vegetable stock. Stir to make sure the potatoes do not stick to the bottom of the pan and bring to the boil. Cover and simmer for about 15 minutes until the vegetables are tender.

Leave to cool a little and then liquidise with a handheld blender or in a blender until smooth.

Add more salt and pepper according to taste. Add more liquid, either stock or milk, to achieve your preferred consistency and then stir in a little cream or crème fraîche. Serve in warmed bowls with crusty bread.

Nutrition per serving

Energy	Protein	Carbs	Sugars
216kcal	**5g**	**38g**	**6g**
Salt	Fibre	Fat	Saturates
1.9g	**6g**	**6g**	**3.4g**

Spicy Lentil and Tomato Soup with Crispy Chorizo

Prep 2 mins Cook 40 mins

Gently spiced and warming, this soup provides a gradual release of energy and helps stabilise blood sugar levels.

We love to eat this sustaining low-GI soup on a Saturday lunchtime, before the boys' rugby matches and my afternoon run. It's brimming with vitamin C, vitamin A and B vitamins, plus important minerals such as magnesium, folic acid and iron.

Ingredients to serve 4–6

2 tbsp olive oil

1 onion, peeled and finely chopped

1 celery stick, finely chopped

1 bay leaf

1 small dried chilli

1 tsp cumin seeds

300g green or brown lentils

1 tbsp balsamic vinegar

800g large can of chopped tomatoes

1 tbsp tomato purée

1½ litres chicken or vegetable stock

salt and freshly ground black pepper

75g chorizo sausage, chopped into small pieces

freshly chopped coriander to decorate

Method

Heat the oil in a large pan and sweat the onion and celery over a very gentle heat for a few minutes until soft. Add the bay leaf, dried chilli and cumin and stir in for 30 seconds.

Add the lentils, vinegar, chopped tomatoes, tomato purée and stock and bring to the boil.

Turn the heat down, cover and simmer for 40 minutes, stirring every 5 minutes or so, until the lentils are tender.

Season with plenty of salt and freshly ground black pepper and check the consistency; you may need to add a little more stock if the soup is too thick.

Meanwhile, heat a frying pan over a medium heat and sauté the chorizo pieces until crisp.

Serve the soup in warmed soup bowls with the chorizo and plenty of chopped coriander sprinkled on top.

Nutrition per serving

Energy	Protein		Carbs	Sugars
443kcal	**25.5g**		**47g**	**9.5g**
Salt	Fibre		Fat	Saturates
2.3g	**11g**		**16g**	**1g**

Butterbean Butternut Soup

Prep 5 mins Cook 40 mins

Wholesome, low in fat, comforting and packed with sustaining carbohydrate.

It's vital for children training intensively to maintain their vitamin and mineral intake; an excellent source of beta carotene, butternut squash also contains plenty of vitamin C, vitamin B1, potassium and other minerals, plus folic acid, omega-3 fatty acids and fibre. Butterbeans are rich in nutrients too, including protein and iron.

Ingredients to serve 4–6

25g unsalted butter

1 tbsp olive oil

1 medium onion, peeled and sliced

1 celery stick, finely chopped

1 tbsp (approx. 35g) finely chopped or grated fresh ginger

1 medium butternut squash, peeled, deseeded and cut up into chunks

salt and freshly ground black pepper to taste

1 litre vegetable stock

400g can butterbeans, drained

1 tbsp lime juice

pinch of chilli powder or paprika

1 tbsp double cream, crème fraîche or extra virgin olive oil to serve

sprinkling of chilli powder or paprika (optional)

Method

Heat the butter and oil in a pan and gently sauté the onion, ginger and celery at the lowest heat for 10 minutes or so until soft.

Add the butternut squash, plenty of salt and pepper, and stir gently to combine with the onion mixture. Add the vegetable stock, bring to the boil and then simmer, covered, for about 30 minutes, until the butternut squash is really tender. Add half the butterbeans after 20 minutes.

Turn off the heat and leave the soup to cool for a few minutes, then blend until the soup is smooth and creamy.

Return the soup to the pan and add the remaining butterbeans. Reheat gently for a few minutes. Check the consistency, adding a little more stock if the soup is too thick. Squeeze in the lime juice, check for seasoning and serve in warmed soup bowls with a drizzle of cream, crème fraîche or olive oil and a sprinkling of chilli powder or paprika, if you like.

Nutrition per serving

Energy	Protein	Carbs	Sugars
339kcal	**10g**	**55g**	**9g**

Salt	Fibre	Fat	Saturates
1.3g	**11.5g**	**11g**	**5g**

Creamy Sweetcorn Soup with Chicken and Mushroom

Prep 2 mins Cook 40 mins

Comforting and nourishing, an excellent soup to prepare in advance for an easy midweek supper.

I'll often make double quantity of this soup, as it seems to disappear before the eyes in the Go Faster Food kitchen. Fairly low in GI, this soup is filling and should provide a good level of sustained energy.

Ingredients to serve 4

2–3 chicken thighs

1 tbsp olive oil

1 small knob butter

1 shallot, finely sliced

2 tsp plain flour

1 litre good-quality chicken or vegetable stock

400g can sweetcorn, including the juice

200g mushrooms, finely sliced

2 tsp mixed herbs

100ml single cream

flat-leaf parsley, roughly chopped

salt and plenty of freshly ground black pepper

Method

Preheat the oven to 180°C/gas mark 4.

Brush the chicken with the olive oil, place on a small roasting dish and roast in the oven for about 30 minutes. When it's cooked, remove the skin and bone from the chicken and chop the meat into small pieces.

Melt the butter in a large pan and very gently sauté the shallot until soft and translucent. Turn off the heat for a minute and stir in the flour.

Gradually stir in the stock and the sweetcorn and bring to the boil. Cover and simmer for about 10 minutes. Leave to cool a little and then blend until really smooth. Pour back into the pan, add the mushrooms, the herbs and the chicken and continue to simmer for a few minutes until the mushrooms become tender. Add a little more stock if the soup is a bit too thick.

Stir in the cream and the parsley, season well and serve in warmed soup bowls.

Nutrition per serving

Energy	Protein	Carbs	Sugars
342kcal	13.5g	37.5g	11.5g

Salt	Fibre	Fat	Saturates
2.1g	3g	15.5g	7g

Serve with warm ciabatta bread and pieces of corn on the cob.

Green Soup

Prep 2 mins Cook 15 mins

This soup is simplicity itself, vibrant in colour and packed with green disease-fighting antioxidants!

Some children who won't eat their greens in the traditional way will quite happily eat them in soup form, especially if accompanied by croutons or a hunk of crusty bread. It's worth persevering; greens are rich in iron, calcium and potassium as well as vitamins C, E and K.

Ingredients to serve 4

25g unsalted butter

1 onion, peeled and diced

1 small potato, peeled and diced

450g spinach, chard, or watercress

600ml chicken of vegetable stock

400ml milk

sea salt and freshly ground black pepper

a little grated lemon zest

¼ tsp grated nutmeg

1 tbsp soured cream or buttermilk

Method

Heat the butter in a large pan and gently sauté the onion for a few minutes. Stir in the potato and sweat for a further few minutes.

Stir in the green vegetables, but reserve a large handful for later. Add the stock and bring to the boil. Cover and simmer gently for about 10 minutes until the potato is cooked.

Add the milk and the remaining handful of greens, remove from the heat and leave to cool for a few minutes. Blend with a handheld blender or in a liquidiser. Add a little more stock or milk if the consistency is too thick.

Season with salt, black pepper, lemon zest and nutmeg, and serve in warmed soup bowls with a swirl of soured cream or buttermilk.

Serve with garlic croutons – brush slices of baguette with olive oil, rub with garlic and bake in the oven for 10 minutes.

Nutrition per serving

Energy	Protein	Carbs	Sugars
167kcal	**10g**	**17g**	**7g**
Salt	Fibre	Fat	Saturates
1g	**2g**	**7g**	**4.5g**

Roasted Pumpkin Soup with Pumpkin Seeds

Prep 2 mins Cook 40 mins

The high-GI carbs in pumpkin are rapidly digested into the bloodstream; great for efficient post-exercise recovery.

Perhaps it's the connection with Halloween, but pumpkin soup is always a favourite with children. Sweet and silky in texture, it makes a warming and nutritious winter supper. Try swapping the pumpkin with butternut or acorn squash if you want to reduce the GI for a more sustaining effect.

Ingredients to serve 4

1 small pumpkin, peeled, deseeded and chopped into chunks (about 900g)

2 sprigs of fresh rosemary

1 garlic clove, unpeeled

2 tbsp olive oil

sea salt and freshly ground black pepper

1 onion, peeled and sliced

25g butter

750ml hot vegetable stock

150ml single cream or milk

squeeze of lime juice

pinch of nutmeg

handful of pumpkin seeds

Method

Preheat the oven to 190°C/gas mark 5.

Place the chopped pumpkin, rosemary sprigs and the garlic clove on a baking tray. Drizzle over the olive oil and, using your hands, make sure all the pumpkin is well coated. Season with salt and black pepper and bake in the oven for 30 minutes, or until the pumpkin is soft, but not too brown.

Remove the pumpkin from the oven, discard the rosemary and squeeze the flesh out of the garlic clove.

Meanwhile, gently sauté the onion in the butter for 5 minutes until soft and translucent. Stir in the garlic and pumpkin, pour in the hot stock and bring to a gentle simmer for a few minutes.

Blend the soup until smooth. Return to the pan and add enough cream or milk to reach a nice consistency; it should not be too thick or it will be cloying. Add the lime juice and nutmeg, and season according to taste.

Toast the pumpkin seeds on a baking tray in the oven for a few minutes. Watch them like a hawk as they can burn easily!

Remove the pumpkin seeds from the oven and serve the soup in warmed bowls with the pumpkin seeds sprinkled on top.

Nutrition per serving

Energy	Protein	Carbs	Sugars
285kcal	**6g**	**25g**	**9g**

Salt	Fibre	Fat	Saturates
1.6g	**7g**	**20g**	**8g**

Slow Roasted Tomato and Basil Soup

Prep 5 mins Cook 2 hours

Intensely tomatoey in flavour, and so much tastier and healthier than the canned variety.

This tomato soup is low in fat and packed with lycopene, vitamins A and C, fibre and potassium, to promote a healthy immune system. Kids love to eat this soup with croutons or cheese on toast.

Ingredients to serve 4

8 medium tomatoes, halved

1 clove garlic, unpeeled

1 tbsp balsamic vinegar

3 tbsp olive oil

1 tsp Demerara sugar

salt and freshly ground black pepper

1 onion, peeled and sliced

1 large carrot, peeled and grated

600ml vegetable stock

400g can chopped tomatoes

1 tbsp tomato purée

1 small dried chilli, flaked (optional)

handful of fresh basil leaves, roughly chopped

Method

Preheat the oven to 150°C/gas mark 2.

Place the tomatoes cut side up on a baking tray with the garlic clove. Sprinkle with the balsamic vinegar, 2 tbsp olive oil, sugar, salt and pepper and bake for 1½ hours, or until the tomatoes are soft and caramelised.

Heat 1 tbsp olive oil in a saucepan. Add the onion and carrot and sauté very gently, with the lid on, for 5 minutes until soft. Stir in the stock and bring to the boil. Reduce to a simmer for a further two minutes. Remove from the heat and blend until smooth. Return to a gentle heat and add the tinned tomatoes, tomato purée and dried chilli, if using.

Remove the tomatoes from the oven, chop them roughly and transfer them to the pan, scraping in the caramelised bits as well. Discard the tomato peel if you like. Bring to a gentle simmer, cover and cook for 20 minutes, stirring frequently, squishing any tomato lumps on the side of the pan. Season according to taste.

We like a lumpier consistency but if you prefer a smooth soup, blend it at this point. If you do, the colour will change to that of a famous brand of canned tomato soup!

Stir in the basil and serve in warmed bowls.

Nutrition per serving

Energy 204kcal	Protein 5g	Carbs 24g	Sugars 15g
Salt 1.3g	Fibre 7g	Fat 12g	Saturates 1.5g

Light Meals

Vegetables, Salads & Sides

Purple-sprouting Broccoli with Poached Egg and Chorizo

Prep 5 mins Cook 8 mins

A delightful, nourishing light lunch, quick to make and bursting with superfood flavour.

Green leafy vegetables are packed with vitamins, riboflavin, folic acid, calcium, iron and other minerals to promote optimum health and to keep the brain functioning well. The addition of the egg, pine nuts and tasty chorizo encourages kids to at least give greens a go.

Ingredients to serve 4
(as a starter or light lunch)

1 tbsp olive oil

100g chorizo sausage, cut into small cubes

200g purple-sprouting broccoli

4 large, free-range eggs

2 tbsp pine nuts, toasted

salt and freshly ground black pepper

fresh bread to serve

For the dressing

1 tbsp extra virgin olive oil

½ tsp coarse grain mustard

½ tbsp balsamic or red wine vinegar

Method

Heat the olive oil in a non-stick frying pan and gently sauté the chorizo until crisp.

Meanwhile, bring a pan of salted water to the boil, add the broccoli and simmer until just tender, for about 2–3 minutes. Drain.

Poach the eggs in a separate pan until the yolks are still soft but the whites are set.

Whisk together the dressing ingredients.

Arrange the broccoli on 4 plates, carefully place an egg onto each plate and scatter over the chorizo and pine nuts. Spoon over the dressing, season with a little salt and pepper, and serve with hunks of fresh bread.

Nutrition per serving

Energy	Protein	Carbs	Sugar
259kcal	**13g**	**4g**	**1.6g**

Salt	Fibre	Fat	Saturates
0.5g	**2g**	**22g**	**5g**

Baby Brussels Sprouts with Crispy Pancetta

Prep 1 min Cook 10 mins

Sweet, tender, baby sprouts, loaded with vitamins C, A and K, as well as fibre and antioxidants.

A million miles away from the cooked-to-oblivion, bitter offerings some of us may remember from our school days. Cooking them in chicken stock makes them sweeter, and the pancetta adds a delicious salty crunch.

Ingredients to serve 4

4 slices of pancetta

25g unsalted butter

450g Brussels sprouts

200ml hot chicken stock

sprig of fresh thyme (optional)

squeeze of lemon juice (optional)

freshly ground black pepper

Method

Grill the pancetta under a medium grill until crispy. Roughly break into pieces and set aside.

Melt the butter in a saucepan over a gentle heat. Add the Brussels sprouts and toss so that they are coated with butter. (There's absolutely no need to cut a cross in these small sprouts, in fact they will go mushy if you do so.)

Sauté gently for 3 minutes, moving the sprouts around the pan frequently. Increase the heat a little and add the hot chicken stock and the thyme, if using.

Bring to the boil, cover and simmer for a couple more minutes until the sprouts are just tender. Drain if there is any stock left in the pan, but the sprouts will probably have soaked up most of this.

Add the pancetta, season with freshly ground black pepper and lemon juice, if using, and serve in a warmed dish.

Nutrition per serving

Energy	Protein	Carbs	Sugar
149kcal	7g	10g	2.6g
Salt	Fibre	Fat	Saturates
1g	2g	10g	5g

I can honestly say kids have been known to fight over these sprouts at the table – they're really that tasty!

Stir-fried Curly Kale with Toasted Almonds

Prep 2 mins Cook 10 mins

This stir-fry brings kids back for seconds!

Glossy, tender and mild in flavour, curly kale takes only minutes to cook. It also contains 6 times more calcium and seven times more vitamin A than broccoli, as well as heaps of vitamin C, with 100g of the cooked leaves far exceeding 50% of a child's RDA.

Ingredients to serve 4

50g flaked almonds

100g chorizo, chopped into pieces (optional)

1 small garlic clove, very finely sliced

1 tbsp olive oil and a small knob of butter

200g curly kale (could use spinach, cavolo nero or Savoy cabbage instead)

sea salt flakes and freshly ground pepper

dried chilli flakes to serve (optional, for those who like a little added fire).

Method

Add the almonds to a large frying pan and dry-roast over a gentle heat, moving them around the pan with a spatula until they are light brown. Remove and set aside for later.

Add the chopped chorizo, if using, and sauté until golden brown. Remove with a slotted spoon and add to the almonds.

Leave the oil from the chorizo in the pan and gently sauté the garlic (add a drop of sunflower oil if you're not using chorizo), until lightly golden, taking care not to burn it. Again, remove and set aside with the almonds and chorizo.

Wipe the pan clean with kitchen paper and then, over a gentle heat, melt the butter with the oil. Add the curly kale and a couple of tablespoons of water. Season with sea salt and freshly ground black pepper and stir-fry for a few minutes until the kale is tender and a glossy, vibrant green.

Return the almonds, chorizo and garlic to the pan and toss together with the kale. Serve sprinkled with a few dried chilli flakes, if you like.

Delicious with lamb chops, chicken, fish, or a poached egg.

Nutrition per serving

Energy 225kcal	Protein 10g	Carbs 6g	Sugar 1g
Salt 1g	Fibre 2g	Fat 19g	Saturates 4.5g

Go Faster Sauté Potatoes

Prep 2 mins Cook 25 mins

Excellent for refuelling the muscles after exercise.

Potatoes vary in glycaemic value; French fries, mashed, baked and sauté potatoes are high GI, making them perfect for post-match recovery, especially if eaten with some protein; a piece of meat or fish for instance. These sauté potatoes are tastier and healthier cooked with their skins on.

Ingredients to serve 4

1kg waxy potatoes, such as Charlotte, unpeeled and cut into chunks

1 tbsp duck fat or rapeseed oil

1 rasher of streaky bacon, chopped quite small (optional)

sea salt

1 tbsp fresh flat-leaf parsley or chives to serve

Method

Start by parboiling the potatoes. Place the potatoes in a pan of salted water, bring to the boil and then simmer for about 5 minutes, until just tender. Using a colander, drain and shake the potatoes about to get rid of any excess water and to create rough edges.

Heat the duck fat or oil in a large frying pan over a medium heat. Add the potatoes and leave them to sauté gently for a few minutes, undisturbed. Add the bacon, then shake the pan around a little. Turn the potato chunks every few minutes until the potatoes are browned all over. This process should take around 20 minutes but it is important not to hurry; the slower the potatoes cook, the more delicious and golden they will be.

When the potatoes are golden brown all over, transfer to a warmed serving dish and sprinkle with sea salt and chopped parsley.

Serve immediately.

Nutrition per serving

Energy	Protein	Carbs	Sugar
239kcal	**6g**	**44g**	**2g**

Salt	Fibre	Fat	Saturates
0.5g	**5.6g**	**5g**	**0.7g**

Recovery Mustard Mash

Prep 2 mins Cook 20 mins

Good-quality sausages, greens and gravy make a perfect accompaniment to this mash.

My daughter was once a fussy eater; she's over that and now far exceeds her 5 a day with her vast appetite for veg. This deliciously creamy mash is one of her first creations after being let loose in the kitchen as a young teen; it's high GI and particularly suitable for post-exercise recovery.

Ingredients to serve 4

1kg floury potatoes, such as Maris Piper, Desiree or King Edward, peeled and halved

25g unsalted butter

250ml milk, warmed

salt and freshly ground black pepper

pinch of nutmeg

1 tbsp coarse-grain mustard

25g bunch of parsley, finely chopped

Method

Place the potatoes in a large pan. Cover them with cold water, bring to the boil and simmer, covered, for about 20 minutes, until the potatoes are really soft.

Drain the potatoes in a colander and leave to cool for a few minutes.

Return the potatoes to the pan and add the butter, milk, salt, pepper and nutmeg. Quickly mash with a fork or a masher until smooth, then stir in the mustard and the parsley.

Nutrition per serving

Energy	Protein	Carbs	Sugar
255kcal	**7g**	**43g**	**6.2g**
Salt	Fibre	Fat	Saturates
0.7g	**6g**	**7g**	**4g**

Potato Rösti

Prep 5 mins Cook 10 mins

Serve with meat, fish, eggs, or even apple sauce, for an excellent post-exercise recovery dish.

For the best, crispiest results, use the larger-holed grater to grate the potatoes, and cold-pressed rapeseed oil for frying. We all prefer to have our own individual cakes, but you can just make one larger one to fit the whole frying pan, if you like.

Ingredients to serve 4

500g potatoes, Maris Piper work well, peeled and grated

1 garlic clove, crushed

25g flat-leaf parsley, finely chopped

sea salt and freshly ground black pepper

1 tbsp rapeseed or sunflower oil for frying

Method

Place the potatoes in a colander and squeeze out the excess liquid.

Combine the potatoes with the garlic, parsley and seasoning in a mixing bowl.

Heat a large non-stick frying pan and add the oil. When it is hot, place dollops of the rösti mixture in the pan and flatten each one out to form a cake. They should not be too thick as this will prevent the potato cooking in the middle.

Fry on a low to medium heat for about 5–7 minutes, until the bottom of the cake is golden brown, then flip over and repeat the process on the other side.

Nutrition per serving

Energy	Protein	Carbs	Sugar
121kcal	**2g**	**20g**	**1.5g**
Salt	Fibre	Fat	*Saturates*
0.5g	**3g**	**4g**	**trace**

Two Potato Mash

Prep 2 mins Cook 20 mins

Despite their sweet flavour, sweet potatoes are medium GI – excellent for maintaining steady blood sugar levels.

Extremely high in antioxidants and an excellent source of vitamin A (beta-carotene), vitamin C, manganese, copper, fibre, potassium and iron, sweet potatoes are surprisingly nutritious. Mashed together with normal potatoes makes a delicious combination.

Ingredients to serve 4

2 medium potatoes, peeled and cut into chunks

1kg sweet potatoes, peeled and cut into chunks

15g butter

squeeze of lime juice

1 tbsp single cream (optional)

salt and freshly ground black pepper

Method

Pop the potatoes and sweet potatoes into a large pan and pour on enough cold water so that they are well covered. Bring to the boil, cover and then turn down the heat to a simmer. Simmer for about 15 minutes, or until the potatoes are really soft, then drain in a colander.

Add the butter (15g is a large knob), a squeeze of lime juice and the single cream, if using, and mash the potatoes with a fork. Season with salt and freshly ground black pepper.

This mash tastes fantastic with spatchcock-roasted chicken with red grapes, page 135.

Nutrition per serving

Energy	Protein	Carbs	Sugar
400kcal	**6g**	**87g**	**2.5g**
Salt	Fibre	Fat	Saturates
0.2g	**13g**	**4g**	**2g**

Sweet Potato Wedges

Prep 2 mins Cook 40 mins

A healthy, very delicious and more sustaining alternative to chips.

Served on their own with a sour cream or guacamole dip, these sweet potato wedges make a nutritious warm snack on a winter's evening.

Ingredients to serve 4

800g sweet potatoes, washed and cut into thick wedges

1 tbsp rapeseed oil

1 pinch paprika

1 tsp dried thyme or rosemary

sea salt and freshly ground black pepper

Method

Preheat the oven to 200°C/gas mark 6.

Soak the sweet potato wedges in cold water for a few minutes, then drain and dry with some kitchen towel.

Toss the sweet potato with the oil, paprika, herbs and salt.

Arrange on a roasting dish, skin side down, and roast for 30–40 minutes until crisp and golden. Sprinkle on some more sea salt and some freshly ground black pepper and serve.

Nutrition per serving

Energy	Protein	Carbs	Sugar
268kcal	**3g**	**56g**	**1g**
Salt	Fibre	Fat	Saturates
0.2g	**8g**	**4g**	-

Bubble and Squeak Cakes

Prep 5 mins Cook 20 mins

A sneaky way to hide greens for reluctant veg eaters!

Prepared either fresh or using leftovers, bubble and squeak makes a delicious post-exercise brunch or lunch. Serve with grilled bacon, a poached egg and some homemade ketchup (see page 164).

Ingredients to serve 4

450g potatoes, peeled and chopped into small chunks

500g Brussels sprouts, greens, Savoy cabbage or peas

2 tbsp rapeseed oil

1 onion, peeled and very finely chopped

100ml milk

salt and freshly ground black pepper

Method

Place the potatoes in a pan of salted cold water, bring to the boil, cover and simmer for about 10 minutes, until the potatoes are tender. Drain thoroughly in a colander.

Meanwhile place the green vegetables in a pan of cold water, bring to the boil and simmer for a few minutes until tender. Drain thoroughly and chop finely.

Heat a drop of oil in a frying pan and gently fry the onion until soft and translucent.

Return the potatoes to the pan, add the milk and mash. Add the chopped greens, the cooked onion, plenty of salt and pepper and mix together. Form little patties of the mixture with your hands.

Heat the rest of the oil in the frying pan, add the patties of bubble and squeak and fry gently for about 5 minutes on each side. Serve hot from the pan.

Nutrition per serving

Energy	Protein		Carbs	Sugar
265kcal	**10g**		**39g**	**10.8g**
Salt	Fibre		Fat	Saturates
0.3g	**9.6g**		**8g**	**1g**

Tomato Ketchup

Prep 2 mins Cook 20 mins

A wholesome and very tasty alternative to the commercial variety.

There's no reason why this ketchup shouldn't be included in the vegetables and salads section. Delicious with Go Faster burgers or as a pasta sauce, this flavoursome tomato ketchup is packed with goodness and very delicious.

Ingredients for 10 servings

400g can of chopped tomatoes

1 tbsp tomato purée

1 tsp olive oil

2 tsp soft brown sugar

1 tsp balsamic vinegar

pinch of salt

pinch of allspice

couple of drops of Tabasco sauce

pinch of ground coriander

freshly ground black pepper

Method

Place all the ingredients in a saucepan, stir to combine and bring to the boil.

Turn the heat down, cover and simmer for about 20 minutes, stirring every now and then, until the sauce is thick and 'ketchuppy'.

Leave to cool, or eat warm with pasta.

Nutrition per serving

Energy	Protein		Carbs	Sugar
14kcal	**0.4g**		**2g**	**1.7g**
Salt	Fibre		Fat	Saturates
trace	**0.5g**		**0.5g**	**trace**

Carrots with White Balsamic & Dijon Dressing

Prep 5 mins No cook

Sweet, crunchy carrots are packed with vitamin C, the disease-fighting antioxidant beta-carotene, as well as bone-building potassium and vitamin K.

Introduced to me as a child by my French family on my first language exchange, this very delicious salad is a traditional children's starter that most French kids will happily tuck into. The white balsamic vinegar is mild and sweet and marries well with the carrot.

Ingredients to serve 4

pinch of salt

1 tsp Dijon mustard

1 tbsp white balsamic vinegar

2 tbsp extra virgin olive oil

5 large carrots, peeled and very finely grated

handful of flat-leaf parsley, very finely chopped

Method

In a small bowl, combine the salt, mustard and balsamic vinegar and then whisk in the oil.

Pour the dressing over the carrots, stir in the parsley and serve.

Nutrition per serving

Energy	Protein	Carbs	Sugar
101kcal	**1g**	**9g**	**4g**
Salt	Fibre	Fat	Saturates
0.2g	**3g**	**7g**	**1g**

Fresh Basil Pesto

Prep 5 mins Cook 5 mins

Shop-bought pesto is fine, but there's no turning back once you've made it from scratch.

Pesto takes moments to make and the end result is totally heavenly. It is also really nutritious. I'll often leave out gnocchi or pasta and pesto for the kids to cook for themselves; it's easy, quite delicious and looks pretty impressive!

Ingredients to serve 4

50g fresh basil leaves

1 small garlic clove, peeled and chopped

pinch of sea salt

50g pine nuts, lightly toasted

freshly ground black pepper

50ml extra virgin olive oil

50g Parmesan, grated

juice of half a lemon, or to taste

Method

Pound the basil leaves with the garlic and salt in a pestle and mortar or food processor.

Add the pine nuts, pepper and olive oil and pound or process again until the required consistency is achieved. Stir in the Parmesan and add a little lemon juice. The balance of ingredients really depends on taste, so don't worry too much about exact quantities.

Delicious tossed with Fresh Go Faster Gnocchi (see page 120), fresh pasta, or grilled chicken breasts.

Nutrition per serving

Energy	Protein	Carbs	Sugar
237kcal	**6g**	**4g**	**1g**

Salt	Fibre	Fat	Saturates
0.1g	**1g**	**23g**	**4g**

Crunchy Rainbow Salad

Prep 5 mins No cook

Simple, colourful, and packed with a wide variety of vitamins and minerals.

This salad is a favourite with those children who prefer their vegetables raw and with a crunch. Serve the dressing on the side if you prefer.

Ingredients to serve 4
(accompaniment to a main meal)

2 large tomatoes

1 orange pepper

½ cucumber

2–3 celery sticks

For the dressing
pinch of caster sugar

pinch of salt

½ tbsp white balsamic vinegar

1 tbsp extra virgin olive oil

small bunch of fresh flat-leaf parsley or coriander leaves, roughly chopped (optional)

Method

Slice the tomatoes, pepper, cucumber and celery as thinly as possible, either with a mandolin if you are feeling brave, with a sharp knife, or with the slicing attachment on a food processor.

Make the dressing; in a small bowl add the sugar and salt to the balsamic vinegar and whisk in the oil.

Pour the dressing over the vegetables, scatter with the fresh herbs, if using, and serve.

Nutrition per serving

Energy	Protein	Carbs	Sugar
68kcal	**2g**	**8g**	**4g**
Salt	Fibre	Fat	Saturates
0.1g	**2.3g**	**4g**	**0.5g**

Dipping Salad with Hummus

Prep 5 mins No cook

A garlicky mush of chickpeas, olive oil and lemon juice; incredibly nutritious for growing athletic kids.

If you can, serve this hummus with crispy salad vegetables in favour of nachos and crisps; a highly effective, if a little sneaky, means of encouraging children to eat more veggies.

Ingredients to serve 4

For the hummus

2 x 400g cans chickpeas.
(drained but reserve the brine)

juice of 2 lemons

2 tbsp tahini

1 garlic clove, peeled and crushed

½ tsp coriander

½ tsp cumin

salt and freshly ground black pepper

2 tbsp olive oil, plus a little extra to drizzle

For the vegetables

A selection of little gem lettuce leaves, carrot sticks, celery sticks, cucumber slices, sticks of red or yellow pepper

Method

Combine the ingredients for the hummus in a food processor and blend until smooth and creamy. You may want to add more lemon juice, coriander, cumin or salt to taste. If it is too thick and stodgy, add a little chickpea brine, or a dash of water.

Transfer to a bowl and drizzle over a little more olive oil. Arrange the vegetables on a plate and serve with the hummus.

Nutrition per serving

Energy	Protein	Carbs	Sugar
261kcal	**11g**	**24g**	-
Salt	Fibre	Fat	Saturates
0.2g	**1.6g**	**14g**	**1.6g**

Sweet Treats

Desserts, Cakes & Energy Bars

Banana and Chunky Chocolate Muffins

Prep 5 mins Cook 25 mins

A tasty and effective snack for post-exercise recovery.

These muffins take minutes to prepare and are surprisingly healthy for such a mouthwatering treat, packed with a good balance of carbohydrate, protein, good fats, fibre and important minerals such as calcium, iron and folic acid. They taste best eaten on the day they are made.

Ingredients for 12 muffins

360g plain flour, sifted

180g caster sugar

1½ tsp baking powder

1 tsp bicarbonate of soda

½ tsp salt

120g milk chocolate chunks, plus 20g to sprinkle on top

2 large, free-range eggs

250ml buttermilk

2 large, ripe bananas, mashed with a fork

80ml melted butter, unsalted

a few drops vanilla essence

Method

Preheat the oven to 180°C/gas mark 4. Line a muffin tray with 12 muffin cases.

Place the flour, sugar, baking powder, bicarbonate of soda, salt and 120g chocolate chunks in a large bowl and mix to combine.

In another bowl, beat the eggs with a fork, then beat in the buttermilk, bananas, melted butter and vanilla.

Add the wet ingredients to the dry ingredients and stir very briefly, just to combine the ingredients. It doesn't matter if the mixture looks lumpy.

Spoon the mixture into the muffin cases, so that they are three quarters full. Sprinkle a few chocolate chunks onto the top of each muffin and bake in the oven for 20–25 minutes, or until the tops are firm to the touch and golden brown.

Leave the muffins to cool in the tray for about 5 minutes and then transfer to a cooling rack.

Freeze brown bananas whole, instead of throwing them out, they work brilliantly in cakes and muffins, defrosted, peeled and mashed.

Nutrition per serving

Energy	Protein		Carbs	Sugars
319kcal	6g		52g	28g
Salt	Fibre		Fat	Saturates
0.8g	1.5g		11g	6g

Banana Malt Loaf

Prep 10 mins Cook 40 mins

Pre-exercise, post-exercise, school breaktime snack, there's always an excuse to eat malt loaf.

Packed with natural sugars, malt extract is extremely high in carbohydrate. It adds a deliciously gooey texture to this banana loaf as well as protein, vitamin A, riboflavin and minerals, such as potassium and phosphorous. This recipe also works with an equivalent amount of runny honey.

Ingredients to serve 12

200g self-raising wholemeal flour

1 tsp ground cinnamon

1 tsp baking powder

pinch of salt

100g soft sunflower margarine

75g soft brown sugar

2 tbsp malt extract

2 large, free-range eggs

2 tbsp buttermilk or natural yoghurt

2 ripe bananas, mashed with a fork

150g raisins

1 tbsp Demerara sugar mixed with ½ tsp ground cinnamon

Method

Preheat the oven to 180°C/gas mark 4 and lightly grease a 1 litre loaf tin.

Put the flour into a bowl with the cinnamon, baking powder and salt.

In another bowl, cream together the margarine, soft brown sugar and malt extract with an electric whisk, until pale and fluffy. Beat in the eggs with the whisk, one at a time. Stir in the buttermilk or yoghurt and the bananas.

Fold in the flour mixture and then finally, fold in the raisins.

Pour the mixture into the tin and sprinkle with the Demerara and cinnamon mix.

Bake for 35–40 minutes until golden brown and springy to the touch.

Place the tin on a wire rack to cool. When cold, remove from the tin, slice and spread with unsalted butter.

Nutrition per serving

Energy	Protein	Carbs	Sugars
229kcal	**4g**	**35g**	**24g**
Salt	Fibre	Fat	Saturates
0.5g	**2.5g**	**8.5g**	**1.5g**

Malt extract was spooned into British children's mouths during the Second World War as a magic elixir to ward off colds and winter illnesses.

Blueberry and Lemon Crumble Muffins

Prep 5 mins Cook 20 mins

Best eaten fresh from the oven, these muffins make a nutritious teatime snack.

Frozen blueberries work well in this recipe. Added to the mixture, straight from the freezer, they keep nice and firm and don't run into the rest of the muffin. Eat these muffins on the day they are baked, or warm them in the oven to freshen them up.

Ingredients for 12 muffins

For the crumble topping

45g plain flour

25g Demerara sugar

1 tsp lemon zest

25g butter, chilled, cubed

10g finely chopped walnuts

For the muffins

250g plain flour

25g cornflour

1 tsp baking powder

100g caster sugar

zest of a lemon

2 large, free-range eggs, lightly beaten

90g melted butter

220ml milk

200g blueberries, dusted with a little flour

Method

Preheat the oven to 180°C/gas mark 4 and line a muffin tray with 12 muffin cases.

Make the topping by rubbing together the flour, sugar, zest and butter until the mixture resembles breadcrumbs. Stir in the chopped walnuts.

Sift together the flour, cornflour and baking powder. Add the sugar and lemon zest.

In a separate bowl, combine the eggs, melted butter, milk and blueberries.

Quickly stir the wet ingredients into the dry ingredients. Spoon into 12 muffin cases, sprinkle over topping and bake for approximately 20 minutes until golden brown.

Nutrition per serving

Energy	Protein	Carbs	Sugars
243kcal	4.5g	34g	13.5g

Salt	Fibre	Fat	Saturates
0.4g	2g	10.5g	6g

Chocolate Biscuit Cake

Prep 10 mins Chill 1 hour

Good nutritious recovery food which will work quickly on tired muscles.

Any combination of dried fruit and nuts work in this recipe, although it's important to use good-quality chocolate. Best kept in the fridge, this iron-rich and wholesome cake will last for several days and works as a great post-training snack.

Ingredients to serve 8

125g plain chocolate (70% cocoa), or a combination of plain and good-quality milk chocolate (eg. Cadbury's Dairy Milk) – for a less rich version

70g unsalted butter

1 tbsp golden syrup

1 tbsp stem ginger syrup

75g Digestive biscuits, broken into small pieces

100g mix of raisins, halved glacé cherries and chopped stem ginger

50g toasted flaked almonds

Method

Grease and line a round 20cm loose-bottomed or spring-form cake tin.

Melt the chocolate in a bowl over a pan of simmering water, then add the butter, the golden syrup and the ginger syrup.

When the butter has melted, take off the heat and leave to cool slightly.

Add the rest of the ingredients and stir to combine.

Spoon out into the cake tin and flatten down.

Chill in the fridge for at least an hour, until set. Cut into slices. Store in the fridge.

Nutrition per serving

Energy	Protein	Carbs	Sugars
369kcal	**4g**	**39g**	**29g**
Salt	Fibre	Fat	Saturates
0.5g	**1g**	**22g**	**11g**

Cherry Pecan Crunch Bars

Prep 10 mins Cook 25 mins

A delicious post-school energy-booster and pre- or post-exercise treat.

With a scrumptious crunch from the pecans and a moist chewiness from the treacly cherries, these bars are nicely balanced with carbohydrate, protein, heart-friendly unsaturated fats, vitamins and minerals, including potassium, magnesium, zinc and calcium.

Ingredients for 12 bars

110g butter

1½ tbsp honey

3 tbsp golden syrup

150g glacé cherries, quartered

60g pecans, roughly chopped, plus 12–16 pecan halves for decoration

225g jumbo porridge oats

1½ tsp ground cinnamon

Method

Preheat the oven to 180°C/gas mark 4. Grease and line a shallow baking tray, 24 x 20cm, or lightly grease a silicon bar mould.

In a saucepan, melt the butter with the honey and golden syrup on a low heat. Then stir in the cherries and the chopped pecans.

Add the porridge oats and cinnamon and mix together really well. Leave to stand for 10 minutes.

Turn the mixture into the tin or spoon into each individual mould and press down with the back of a spoon or your fingers. Decorate with the pecan halves by pressing them lightly into the mixture.

Bake in the oven for 20–25 minutes until golden. Remove the tin from the oven and set on a wire rack. Leave to cool slightly and then mark into bars with a really sharp knife. If you remove the bars from the tin too soon they won't stick together, so try to resist eating them until cool and firm!

Nutrition per serving

Energy	Protein	Carbs	Sugars
225kcal	**3g**	**28g**	**3.9g**
Salt	Fibre	Fat	Saturates
0.1g	**2.6g**	**12.6g**	**5.2g**

Perfect for back-to-back training, to replenish depleted glycogen stores and help tired muscles recover quickly.

Go Faster Energy Bars

Prep 5 mins Cook 1 hour

Energy-boosting goodness in every bite!

Crammed with fruit, nuts and seeds, these incredibly nutritious bars keep well in an airtight container for days. Sweetened condensed milk and peanut butter are used as a binder instead of butter and syrup, but for those with peanut allergies, use almond or cashew butter as an alternative.

Ingredients for 12 bars

1 x 397g can condensed milk

1 tbsp crunchy peanut butter

80g pumpkin or sunflower seeds or mixture

20g poppy seeds

150g mixture of chopped dates, sultanas and cranberries

100g desiccated coconut (optional)

240g porridge oats (half refined, half jumbo)

Method

Preheat the oven to 140°C/gas mark 1. Grease and line an 18 x 25cm baking tray.

Pour the condensed milk into a saucepan and gently warm through. Stir in the peanut butter.

Add the rest of the ingredients and spoon into the baking tray. Bake in the oven for 50 minutes to 1 hour, until golden brown.

Nutrition per serving

Energy	Protein	Carbs	Sugars
339kcal	**8g**	**42g**	**27.5g**
Salt	Fibre	Fat	Saturates
0.1g	**4.5g**	**15.5g**	**7.5g**

Marmalade Flapjacks

Prep 5 mins Cook 20 mins

Pre-exercise, post-exercise, teatime snack... there's always an excuse to eat a flapjack!

These flapjacks are surprisingly light and not too sweet. Thick-cut marmalade, with lots of lumps of oranges in it, creates a slightly chewy texture with a deliciously caramelised flavour.

Ingredients for 12 flapjacks

75g unsalted butter

2 tbsp Demerara sugar

2 tbsp golden syrup

2 tbsp thick-cut marmalade

225g porridge oats
(half jumbo/half traditional)

Method

Preheat the oven to 180°C/gas mark 4. Lightly grease a 20cm square shallow baking tray.

Melt the butter in a large pan, then add the sugar, syrup and marmalade, cook on a very low heat until the sugar is dissolved.

Add the porridge oats and stir well to combine. Turn off the heat.

Transfer to a baking tray and press down with the back of a spoon or your fingers. Bake in the oven for 20 minutes until golden brown.

Leave the flapjacks to cool for about 10 minutes and then mark into fingers or squares with a really sharp knife.

Remove the flapjacks from the tin when they are completely cool and firm.

Nutrition per serving

Energy	Protein	Carbs	Sugars
161kcal	**2.5g**	**23g**	**11g**

Salt	Fibre	Fat	Saturates
0.1g	**2g**	**7g**	**3.5g**

Go Faster Date, Apricot and Sunflower Seed Flapjacks

Prep 10 mins Cook 20 mins

Crisp and crunchy on the outside, gooey and moist on the inside, and crammed with hidden goodness.

I chop everything very finely for children who say they don't like dried fruit or the texture of nuts. A little devious but it usually works! Make a batch of these to pop into the lunch box or to munch on the journey to the sports fixture.

Ingredients for 12 bars

75g butter

1 tbsp soft light brown sugar

2 tbsp golden syrup (dip the spoon in hot water before using so the syrup is easier to pour)

75g mix of dried apricots and dates, without stones, chopped as finely as possible

50g sunflower seeds

zest of a lemon

200g porridge oats
(half jumbo/half traditional)

Method

Preheat the oven to 170°C/gas mark 3. Grease and line a 20cm square shallow cake tin.

In a pan, melt the butter with the sugar and syrup on a low heat and, when the sugar has dissolved, add the fruit and sunflower seeds, lemon zest and then the porridge oats. Mix together really well. If the mixture seems sloppy, add another handful of oats.

Turn the mixture into the tin and press down with the back of a spoon or your fingers.

Bake the flapjacks for 15–20 minutes until golden. Remove the tin from the oven and place on a wire rack.

Leave to cool for 10 minutes or so and then mark into fingers or squares with a really sharp knife.

Remove the flapjacks from the tin when they are completely cool and firm. No doubt several will have disappeared by this time…

Nutrition per serving

Energy	Protein	Carbs	Sugars
180kcal	**3g**	**18g**	**10g**

Salt	Fibre	Fat	Saturates
0.1g	**1.5g**	**11g**	**4g**

Chia Seed Energy Balls

Prep 5 mins No cook

Little balls of delicious goodness which take moments to make.

Dried fruit, rich in dietary fibre, vitamins and essential minerals, and packed with natural sugars to revitalise the body with a quick nutrient-rich energy boost, is 'mushed' up in the food processor with a variety of seeds and chia*, an unbelievably rich source of protein, carbohydrate, omega-3 fatty acids, antioxidants and phytonutrients.

Ingredients for 20 balls

50g soft, pitted dates, chopped

60g soft dried apricots, chopped

80g sultanas

1 tbsp milled chia seeds

40g pumpkin seeds

20g sunflower seeds

1 dessertspoon runny honey

2 tbsp sesame seeds, or desiccated coconut

*Chia can be found in some supermarkets, in high street health stores and online.

Method

Place the chia, pumpkin and sunflower seeds into a food processor and whizz until finely chopped. Add the dried fruit and whizz again until the mixture starts to stick together.

Add the honey and combine.

Roll into small balls in the palm of your hands, about 1½cm in diameter.

Pour the sesame seeds into a small bowl and then roll each ball in the sesame seeds to cover completely. (You can use desiccated coconut if you prefer). These will keep for a couple of weeks stored in a plastic bag or airtight container.

Chia is a dietary staple of the Mexican Tarahumara tribe, these incredible people run miles and miles over mountain ranges with seemingly endless energy.

Nutrition per serving

Energy	Protein	Carbs	Sugars
51kcal	**1.4g**	**6.4g**	**4.3g**
Salt	Fibre	Fat	Saturates
0.25g	**1.4g**	**2.5g**	**0g**

Coconut and Carrot Cake with Honey Yoghurt Icing

Prep 15 mins Cook 1 hour

Moist, wholesome and very tasty!

Absolutely brimming with goodness, this delicious cake keeps for days and works well as a post-school energy booster. Best kept in the fridge because of the yoghurt icing, you will find the cake improves in flavour over a couple of days.

Ingredients to serve 12

For the cake

100g raisins

225g unsalted butter (softened)
or soft margarine

225g soft brown sugar

zest and juice of one lemon

4 large, free-range eggs

225g self-raising wholemeal flour, sifted

1 tsp baking powder

1 tsp cinnamon

½ tsp salt

50g desiccated coconut

250g carrots, peeled and finely grated

For the icing

2 tbsp soft cream cheese

1 tbsp Greek yoghurt

2 tbsp runny honey

a few walnuts to decorate (optional)

Method

Preheat the oven to 180°C/gas mark 4. Grease and line a 23cm diameter round springform cake tin.

Put the raisins into a small bowl and pour over just enough boiling water to cover. (When making this cake for adults I often use half boiling water, half sloe gin or sherry).

Cream the butter, sugar and lemon zest together until light and fluffy. Add the eggs, beating well as you add each one.

Fold in the flour, baking powder, cinnamon and salt with a metal tablespoon. Fold in the coconut, carrots, lemon juice and raisins, including the raisin water.

Pour into the cake tin and bake for about 1 hour, or until the cake comes away from the side of the cake tin and a skewer inserted into the middle of the cake comes out clean.

Remove from the oven and leave to cool in the tin for five minutes. Turn out onto a wire rack until completely cool.

Cream the cheese, yoghurt and the honey together and spread generously over the cake. Decorate with whole or chopped walnuts, if you like.

Nutrition per serving

Energy	Protein	Carbs	Sugars
408kcal	**7g**	**42g**	**30.5g**
Salt	Fibre	Fat	Saturates
0.9g	**4g**	**25g**	**14.5g**

Go Faster Carrot Cake

Prep 15 mins Cook 1¼ hours

An all-time favourite Go Faster Food training snack, which goes down well with kids and adults alike.

Really moist, filling and packed with flavour, this cake is extremely nutritious and keeps well for a few days in a cake tin. A large cake, I often make this in advance for when friends come to stay for the weekend, adding the icing at the last minute.

Ingredients to serve 12

For the cake

250g unsalted butter

375g sugar (half caster, half Demerara)

zest of 2 oranges

4 large, free-range eggs

450g carrots, peeled and grated

150g mix of raisins and dried cranberries

100g walnuts, roughly chopped

juice of 1 orange

250g self-raising wholemeal flour, sifted

1 tsp bicarbonate of soda

1½ tsp mixed spice

1 tsp salt

For the icing

225g full-fat soft cheese

40g unsalted butter, at room temperature

80–100g icing sugar

squeeze of lemon or lime juice

small handful whole or chopped walnuts to decorate

Method

Preheat the oven to 170°C/gas mark 3–4. Grease and line a 20cm square tin or 23cm round springform cake tin.

Cream the butter, sugar and orange zest together until light and fluffy. Add the eggs, beating well as you add each one.

Fold in the grated carrots, raisins, cranberries and nuts, and add the orange juice.

Fold in the flour, bicarbonate of soda, spice and salt.

Pour into the cake tin and bake for about 1¼ hours. Baking time depends on the juiciness of the carrots, but you will know the cake is done as the cake comes away from the side of the cake tin and a skewer inserted into the middle of the cake comes out clean.

Turn the cake out onto a wire rack to cool.

To make the icing, cream the cheese and butter together. Add the icing sugar and lemon juice and beat until smooth. Spread the icing generously over the cake. Decorate with whole or chopped walnuts.

Nutrition per serving

Energy	Protein	Carbs	Sugars
588kcal	**8g**	**65g**	**53g**
Salt	Fibre	Fat	Saturates
1.3g	**3g**	**33g**	**18g**

Chocolate Chip and Courgette Cupcakes

Prep 10 mins Cook 35 mins

A sneaky way to your five a day, packed with vitamins A and C and iron.

These fabulously moist, fudgy chocolate cupcakes were recently devoured by my son and a bunch of his 12-year-old friends within minutes of their return from a mountain bike ride. They had no idea that they were eating courgettes! Delicious for dessert, with a dollop of cream and fresh raspberries.

Ingredients for 12 cup cakes

175g 70% dark chocolate, melted, plus 50g cut into small chunks

2 large, free-range eggs

125g caster sugar

200g sunflower or rapeseed oil

225g courgettes, skins on, finely grated and squeezed of excess water

200g self-raising flour, sifted

1 tsp ground cinnamon

1 tsp bicarbonate of soda

For the frosting (optional)
140g icing sugar

140g unsalted butter, softened

100g 70% dark chocolate

Method

Preheat the oven to 190°C/gas mark 5. Arrange 12 muffin cases in a muffin tin.

Melt 175g chocolate in a heatproof bowl over a pan of simmering water. Break the eggs into a clean mixing bowl. Add the sugar and oil and beat until pale and thick. Fold in the melted chocolate with a metal spoon and then fold in the courgettes, flour, cinnamon, bicarbonate of soda and 50g of chocolate chunks.

Divide the mixture between the 12 muffin cases and bake in the oven for about 30–35 minutes until well-risen and cooked through.

To make the frosting, melt 100g chocolate in a heatproof bowl over a pan of simmering water and leave to cool. Beat the icing sugar and butter together until smooth, pour in the melted chocolate and beat well.

Remove the cakes from the oven when cooked and leave to cool on a wire rack.

Ice the cakes with the frosting when they are completely cold. Decorate with fudge pieces, if you like.

Nutrition per serving

Energy	Protein	Carbs	Sugars
354kcal	**4.4g**	**30.3g**	**16.1g**
Salt	Fibre	Fat	Saturates
0.3g	**2.5g**	**24.7g**	**6g**

Lemon Drizzle Crust Cake

Prep 10 mins Cook 25 mins

A delightfully soft buttery sponge with a crusty sugary topping, packed with citrus vitamin C.

Tangy and very delicious, this cake is really straightforward to make. You could also serve it as a dessert, cut into squares, with a scoop of ice cream and some blueberries. For a less tangy flavour, swap the lemon juice and zest with orange.

Ingredients to make 12 slices

175g unsalted butter

175g caster sugar

zest of one lemon, grated

2 large, free-range eggs

175g self-raising flour, sifted

For the crust
juice of 2 lemons

100g sugar

Method

Preheat the oven to 180°C/gas mark 4. Grease and line an 18 x 25cm baking tin.

Cream the butter, sugar and lemon zest together until light and fluffy. Add the eggs, beating well as you add each one.

Fold in the flour and spoon the mixture into the cake tin, (don't worry that the mixture is quite firm, the lemon juice poured over after cooking renders the cake nicely moist). Bake in the oven for about 25 minutes until golden brown and cooked through.

Take the cake out of the oven, mix the lemon juice and the sugar together and spoon over the cake immediately.

Cool in the tin for 30 minutes or so. Cut into squares and serve.

Deliciously moist, very light and extremely quick and easy to make.

Nutrition per serving

Energy	Protein	Carbs	Sugars
262kcal	2.5g	35.5g	24.5g
Salt	Fibre	Fat	Saturates
0.3g	0.5g	13g	8g

Spanish Almond and Orange Cake

Prep 10 mins Cook 35 mins

A natural energy food, containing just three basic ingredients.

Made from almonds, sugar and eggs (yes, no flour, no butter!), this fabulous almond and orange cake, rich in cholesterol-reducing monounsaturated fats, vitamin C and E, plus magnesium and potassium, makes an effective energy booster or post-exercise treat to replenish muscles with carbohydrate, protein and lost minerals.

Ingredients to serve 6–8

4 large, free-range eggs, separated

zest of 1 large orange

225g caster sugar

225g ground almonds

½ tsp cinnamon

1 tbsp freshly squeezed orange juice

icing sugar to decorate

Method

Preheat the oven to 180°C/gas mark 4. Lightly grease a 23cm springform cake tin or flan dish with butter.

Whisk the egg whites to soft peak stage with an electric whisk.

Put the egg yolks, orange zest and sugar into a separate bowl and whisk until pale and creamy. Stir in the almonds, the cinnamon and the orange juice.

Fold in the egg whites with a metal spoon, a little at a time.

Pour the mixture into the cake tin and cook in the oven for about 30–35 minutes, until golden. If you poke a skewer into the middle of the cake, it should come out clean. Cool in the tin, on a wire rack.

When cool, decorate with icing sugar. Enjoy with fresh fruit and a dollop of crème fraîche.

Based on the traditional 'Tarta de Santiago', offered to refuel pilgrims on arrival in Santiago de Compostela, Spain, at the end of their arduous pilgrimage from France..

Nutrition per serving

Energy	Protein	Carbs	Sugars
323kcal	**9g**	**31g**	**30g**
Salt	Fibre	Fat	Saturates
0.1g	**2g**	**18g**	**2g**

Anzac Cookies

Prep 5 mins Cook 20 mins

A melt-in-the-mouth mid-morning or pre-exercise energy boost.

These oat cookies were traditionally baked by anxious Australian wives and mothers during World War I. They were packed in food parcels, and sent to boost the morale of the Australian soldiers in the trenches in Europe. My grandfather was one of these soldiers.

Ingredients for 12–15 cookies

85g unsalted butter

35g golden syrup

½ tsp bicarbonate of soda

½ tbsp boiling water

60g jumbo rolled oats

70g plain flour

60g desiccated coconut

60g caster sugar

pinch of salt

Method

Preheat the oven to 160°C/gas mark 3 and lightly grease a large, flat baking tray.

Gently melt the butter and the golden syrup in a pan.

Dissolve the bicarbonate of soda in the boiling water and stir it into the melted butter and syrup mixture.

Combine the other ingredients in a separate bowl and then pour into the pan. Stir to combine.

Form walnut-sized balls of the mixture and place onto the baking tray, allowing room for them to spread.

Bake in the oven for 15–20 minutes until light golden brown.

Cool for a few minutes in the tin and then transfer to a wire rack to cool completely. They will crisp up as they cool.

These delicious cookies keep for several days in an airtight container.

Nutrition per serving

Energy	Protein	Carbs	Sugars
154kcal	**1.5g**	**16g**	**8g**
Salt	Fibre	Fat	Saturates
0.4g	**2g**	**9.5g**	**6.5g**

Raspberry Almond Crumble

Prep 5 mins Cook 35 mins

Raspberries and almonds – a totally delicious combo, and packed with goodness.

A rich source of the antioxidant vitamin E, ground almonds make a healthy and tasty crumble topping alternative to flour. If you want to go gluten-free, then replace all the flour with ground almonds.

Ingredients to serve 4–6

75g cold unsalted butter, cut into small cubes

100g ground almonds

75g plain wholemeal flour

75g Demerara sugar

1 tsp cinnamon

400g pack of frozen raspberries

1 tbsp sugar, or according to taste

handful of flaked almonds

hot custard to serve

Method

Preheat the oven to 200°C/gas mark 6.

Make the crumble mixture. Rub together the butter, ground almonds and flour until the mixture looks and feels like breadcrumbs. Stir in the Demerara sugar and the cinnamon.

Arrange the raspberries in an ovenproof pie dish (use raspberries straight from the freezer without defrosting them) and sprinkle with 1 tbsp sugar.

Spoon the crumble mixture over the top of the raspberries, scatter with a handful of flaked almonds and cook in the oven for about 35 minutes. Serve with hot custard.

I always think it's a pity to cook fresh raspberries, so use a pack of frozen ones for this recipe, much cheaper and very tasty.

Nutrition per serving

Energy	Protein		Carbs	Sugars
332kcal	**7g**		**29g**	**20.5g**
Salt	Fibre		Fat	Saturates
0.3g	**5.5g**		**22g**	**8g**

Go Faster Recovery Rice Pudding

Prep 2 mins Cook 1½–2 hours

The ultimate high-GI recovery food.

A favourite post-run treat of double Olympian and Commonwealth bronze medallist marathon runner Liz Yelling, who's a firm supporter of Go Faster Food, this recipe gets serious amounts of carbohydrate into the system quickly to restore muscles after a big event or training session.

Ingredients to serve 4

100g short-grain pudding rice

1 litre semi-skimmed milk

2 tbsp caster sugar

¼ tsp nutmeg

½–1 tsp cinnamon (or 1 cinnamon stick)

1 bay leaf (optional)

1 tsp Demerara to serve

Method

Method One – Creamed Rice

Mix all the ingredients together in a heavy-based pan and bring to the boil.

Simmer on the lowest heat possible, using a diffuser if you have one, for about 1–1¼ hours, stirring frequently until the rice has absorbed the milk and the texture is thick and creamy.

Sprinkle with a little Demerara sugar to serve.

Method Two – Rice Pudding

Preheat the oven to 180°C/gas mark 4.

Mix all the ingredients in a lightly buttered oven dish and place in the oven.

After 30 minutes, stir to prevent the rice from sticking together.

Turn the oven down to 150°C/gas mark 2, sprinkle a little sugar on the top and bake for another 1½ hours until a lovely brown skin has formed on the surface.

Nutrition per serving

Energy	Protein	Carbs	Sugars
250kcal	**10g**	**44g**	**23g**
Salt	Fibre	Fat	Saturates
0.3g	**neg**	**5g**	**3g**

Blueberry Yoghurt Ice Cream

Prep 5 mins Churn 30 mins in ice-cream maker

Deep purple in colour and brimming with blueberry goodness.

Ice creams not only make an easy dessert for the family, but they can also be a surprisingly healthy option. Although possible to make this ice cream by hand, an ice-cream maker does the hard work for you, producing really impressive and professional results.

Ingredients to serve 10
(to fill a 1 litre tub)

150g golden caster sugar

zest of 1 lime

60ml lime juice

400g bag of frozen blueberries

500g pot ready-made custard

500g pot Greek yoghurt

1 tbsp runny honey

Method

Dissolve the sugar with the lime juice and zest in a pan over a very gentle heat.

Add the blueberries and stir until defrosted. Bring to the boil and simmer for a couple of minutes until syrupy. Leave to cool.

In a large bowl, combine the blueberry mixture with the custard, Greek yoghurt and honey.

Churn in an ice-cream maker until thick and smooth, then pour into a 1 litre plastic container and freeze.

If you don't have an ice-cream maker, then pour into a 1 litre plastic container, cover and freeze for two hours, then blend in a food processor until smooth and creamy and return to the plastic container and freeze again until required. The more times you repeat this process, the better results you will have.

Nutrition per serving

Energy	Protein		Carbs	Sugars
204kcal	**4g**		**32g**	**27g**
Salt	Fibre		Fat	Saturates
0.1g	**1.2g**		**6.5g**	**0.8g**

Some reluctant fruit eaters will quite happily tuck into fruit in the guise of ice cream!

Lemon Curd Frozen Yoghurt

Prep 1 min Churn 30 mins in ice-cream maker

Smooth, citrusy, creamy and packed with vitamin C.

Some shop-bought ice cream is packed with sugar, saturated fat-laden double cream and unwanted additives, just read the ingredients label of a pot in your freezer to see for yourself! This homemade ice cream is a healthier alternative and makes an excellent post-exercise recovery treat for a summer's day.

Ingredients to serve 4-6
(to fill a 1 litre tub)

300g jar of good-quality lemon curd

zest of one lemon

500g pot Greek yoghurt

Method

Combine the ingredients and churn in an ice-cream maker until thick and smooth, then pour into a 1 litre plastic container and freeze.

If you don't have an ice-cream maker, then pour into a 1 litre plastic container, cover and freeze for two hours, then blend in a food processor until smooth and creamy and return to the plastic container and freeze again until required. The more times you repeat this process, the better results you will have.

Add a spoonful of this to cold milk and fruit to make a delicious smoothie.

Nutrition per serving

Energy	Protein	Carbs	Sugars
226kcal	**3g**	**32g**	**29g**

Salt	Fibre	Fat	Saturates
trace	**-**	**11g**	**1.3g**

Strawberry Sorbet

Prep 5 mins Churn 30 mins in ice-cream maker

A mouth-wateringly refreshing sorbet, ideal for rehydrating after a hot day's training.

Made in an ice-cream maker, this colourful vibrant red sorbet is fat-free, dairy-free and egg-free, and packed with flavoursome vitamin C; a perfect treat for a summer's afternoon or light dessert.

Ingredients to serve 10
(to fill a 1 litre tub)

400ml water

125g sugar

600g fresh or frozen strawberries, stalks removed and chopped

2 tbsp orange juice

1 tbsp lemon juice

Method

In a small saucepan, gently heat the water and sugar until the sugar dissolves. Bring to the boil and simmer for a minute or so until syrupy.

Stir in the strawberries and leave to cool.

Add the orange and lemon juice and churn in an ice-cream maker until smooth. Pour into a 1 litre plastic container and freeze. Remove from the freezer to soften a little about 20 minutes before serving.

If you don't have an ice-cream maker, then blend all the ingredients together in a food processor once the sugar syrup and strawberry combination is cool. Pour into a 1 litre plastic container, cover and freeze for two hours, then blend again, until smooth and creamy, return to the plastic container and freeze again until required. The more times you repeat this process, the better results you will have.

Nutrition per serving

Energy	Protein	Carbs	Sugars
70kcal	-	**18g**	**16g**
Salt	Fibre	Fat	Saturates
-	**1.2g**	-	-

For a homemade slush puppy, scoop into a chilled glass and stir until slushy enough to drink.

Energy Smoothies & Recovery Shakes

Banana, Mango and Pineapple Power Punch

Prep 5 mins

Low to medium GI to power a child through an early morning's training session.

This smoothie is a practical solution for children who can't face anything solid first thing in the morning. Protein, a hefty portion of beta-carotene, folic acid, fibre, B vitamins, vitamin C, calcium and other essential minerals will promote alertness, concentration and energy. If you can, chill all the ingredients first.

Ingredients for 2 glasses

8 ice cubes

1 ripe mango, peeled, stoned and chopped

½ fresh or frozen pineapple, peeled, cored and chopped

1 small banana or ½ a large banana, chopped

juice of ½–1 lime (according to taste)

150ml skimmed milk

Method

Crush the ice cubes in the blender and then add the rest of the ingredients.

Blend until smooth. If the smoothie is too thick, add a little more cold milk.

Pour into two long glasses and drink.

Nutrition per serving

Energy	Protein	Carbs	Sugars
180kcal	**4g**	**40g**	**40g**
Salt	Fibre	Fat	Saturates
0.1g	**4.5g**	**1g**	**neg**

Blueberry Blast

Prep 2 mins

An excellent carbohydrate-to-protein ratio to help muscles recover after exercise.

Rich in vitamin C and calcium, this tasty smoothie makes a sustaining and satisfying breakfast drink or after-school refresher too.

Ingredients for 2 glasses

150g blueberries, fresh or frozen

250g natural yoghurt

200ml milk

2 tsp runny honey

2 drops of vanilla extract

4 ice cubes

Method

Put everything in the blender and whizz until smooth. Taste for sweetness and add more honey if required.

Pour into two long glasses and drink.

Nutrition per serving

Energy	Protein	Carbs	Sugar
191kcal	**8.3g**	**27g**	**24g**
Salt	Fibre	Fat	Saturates
0.2g	**1.8g**	**6g**	**4g**

Strawberry Super Smoothie

Prep 2 mins

A vivid-red smoothie that's rich in potassium.

Packed with phytonutrients and vitamin C, this smoothie will give you a boost at any time of day – at breakfast, before training or to rehydrate afterwards.

Ingredients for 2 glasses

20–30 strawberries (about 200–250g), stalks removed and chopped

200ml apple juice

2 drops of balsamic vinegar

½ tsp icing sugar or to taste

½ kiwi fruit, peeled and chopped (optional)

4 ice cubes

Method

Put everything in the blender and whizz until smooth.

Pour into two long glasses and drink.

Nutrition per serving

Energy	Protein	Carbs	Sugars
104kcal	**1g**	**25g**	**20g**
Salt	Fibre	Fat	Saturates
trace	**2.3g**	**0.2g**	**-**

Fruit Salad Refresher

This smoothie will boost both body and brain!

With copious amounts of vitamin C, carbohydrate, calcium, potassium and fibre, this fruit salad in a glass will wake kids up in the morning!

Ingredients for 2 glasses

1 banana, peeled and chopped

5 strawberries, stalks removed and chopped

1 kiwi fruit, peeled and chopped

100g yoghurt or milk

80ml pineapple juice

100ml orange juice

1 tsp honey

Method

Put everything in the blender and whizz until smooth. Taste for sweetness and add more honey if required.

Pour into two long glasses and drink.

Nutrition per serving

Energy	Protein	Carbs	Sugars
178kcal	**5g**	**39g**	**27g**

Salt	Fibre	Fat	Saturates
trace	**3.3g**	**1.2g**	**0.6g**

Banana Recovery Shake

For efficient muscle recovery and repair.

With an ideal carbohydrate to protein ratio to kick-start the recovery process after a long workout, this simple shake is quickly and easily digested. It's also light on the stomach, virtually fat-free and packed with vitamin C, B6 and essential minerals such as potassium and calcium. Most kids love it!

Ingredients for 1 large glass

1 egg white

1 banana, the riper the better for recovery

2 ice cubes or a tbsp crushed ice

200ml skimmed milk

1 tsp honey

3 tsp drinking chocolate or a squeeze of lime juice (optional)

Method

Separate the yolk from the egg white and pour the egg white into the blender. Roughly chop a banana and add to the blender. Add the ice, milk, honey and drinking chocolate or lime juice, if using. Blend at full speed until smooth. Pour into a chilled glass and drink.

Nutrition per serving

Energy	Protein	Carbs	Sugars
207kcal	**11g**	**43g**	**17g**

Salt	Fibre	Fat	Saturates
0.1g	**3.5g**	**0.5g**	**neg**

Kiwi Pear Chia
Protein Boost

Prep 2 mins

Energising and totally natural, this drink is a blast of sustaining nourishment.

Milled chia* is not only rich in protein, it is also a source of short-chain plant-based omega-3 fats and minerals, in particular iron, calcium, magnesium and phosphorous. Completely tasteless, a sneaky spoonful added to smoothies, soups and sauces provides a seriously nutritional energy punch.

Ingredients for 2 glasses

4 kiwis, peeled and chopped

2 ripe pears, peeled, cored and chopped

1 small banana

100ml milk

100g natural yoghurt

1 egg white

1 tbsp milled chia seed

3–4 tsp runny honey (or to taste)

4 ice cubes

*Chia can be found in some supermarkets, in high street health stores and online.

Method

Put everything in the blender and whizz until smooth. Taste for sweetness and add more honey if required.

Pour into two long glasses and drink.

Nutrition per serving

Energy	Protein		Carbs	Sugars
353kcal	**10g**		**74g**	**45g**
Salt	Fibre		Fat	Saturates
0.2g	**15g**		**5g**	**1.8g**

INDEX